Beyond the Bikesheds

Fresh approaches to fieldwork in the school locality

Beyond the Bikesheds

Fresh approaches to fieldwork in the school locality

David Job, Clare Day and Tony Smyth

The
Geographical
Association

Acknowledgements

The authors are very grateful to members of the Geographical Association's Secondary Education Section Committee who contributed ideas to this book. We would also like to acknowledge the help of Tony Thomas, Director of the Field Studies Council, and Dave Hassell, Chair of the IT Working Group, for assistance with the ICT content.

The Geographical Association would like to thank the following individuals and organisations for photographs:

BECTa (pages 22 and 26), David Boardman (page 37), British Wind Energy Society (page 58), Clare Day (page 34), Chris Garnett (pages 12, 28, 38, 48), Elaine Jackson (page 8), Michael Jay/MJP Geopacks (page 70), Steve Pratchett (page 40), Helen Sail (page 46), Martin Shevill (page 18), Sustrans/Paul Osborne/Julia Bayne (pages 2, 66) and Mo Wilson/Format (page 74).

ISBN 1 899085 71 8
First published 1999
Impression number 10 9 8 7 6 5 4 3 2 1
Year 2002   2001   2000   1999

Published by the Geographical Association, 160 Solly Street, Sheffield S1 4BF. The Geographical Association is a registered charity: no 313129.

The Publications Officer of the GA would be happy to hear from other potential authors who have ideas for geography books. You may contact the Officer via the GA at the address above.

Designed by ATG Design, Catalyst Creative Imaging.
Printed and bound by Redwood Books.

Contents

Introduction

The main intention of this book is to offer fresh ideas, strategies, frameworks and practical support to teachers organising fieldwork in the school locality for key stage 3 and key stage 4/GCSE. In considering both the organisation and purposes of fieldwork, it is helpful to distinguish between residential fieldwork which involves one or more nights away from home, those visits to specific sites where students are taken some distance from school for a whole day, and fieldwork within the school locality, which can be accomplished without significant adjustment to the timetable.

Fieldwork within the school locality, the focus of this book, is open to a number of interpretations. For our purposes it includes activities:

● within the school buildings (but outside the classroom),
● in the school grounds, and
● beyond the school gates in the immediate locality accessible on foot.

While this is a practical definition, the distinction between operating within and beyond the school gates needs to be appreciated from the point of view of health and safety and specific school policies concerning supervision.

Most geography teachers relish the opportunities of fieldwork away from the school and home locality. The attractions include: allowing students to experience a novel milieu, the motivation which comes from learning together in a contrasting environment, the social aspects of a residential fieldcourse, and the aesthetic and emotional experiences of being in fine landscapes which can form the inspiration for a lifelong interest in geography. We do not suggest that local fieldwork can replace the opportunities which residential fieldwork offers, rather it extends the fieldwork experiences of students by offering frequent, affordable and purposeful outdoor experiences.

At first sight, fieldwork closer to home may seem less appealing. For many of us the milieu may appear drab, familiar, divorced from the natural world with limited opportunities for exploring ideas in physical geography. Yet if we examine some of the changing priorities in geography eduation, there may be certain purposes, which are more readily achieved through local fieldwork than the one-off visit to a more distant place.

We should envisage the field experience not just as a foray into the outdoors to collect data, but as a spiral of learning in which our initial visit is one of open-ended discovery. Working as close to school as possible enables return visits for more objective investigation, enquiry or data collection. If we are interested in promoting a concern for quality of life, social equity or the conservation of valued habitats or townscapes in our localities, then working locally may allow us to extend the outcomes of our investigations into participating for change for a better world in the context of our local communities and environments. Local fieldwork then encompasses not only aspects of the geography national curriculum and related skills, but also the often neglected cross-curricular themes of citizenship and environmental education.

In these contexts, even more familiar fieldwork activities of counting traffic or surveying shopping habits can, with new twists, become much more than just techniques to learn (see pages 67-69 and 71-73).

The structure of this book

Part One of this book overviews the purposes, strategies and practices of local fieldwork, as well as discussing the opportunities that working in the local environment offers. Chapter 1 reviews the *why* of fieldwork – the diversity of purposes which geographers have associated with fieldwork. The *how* of fieldwork is then considered in Chapter 2 through a review of the evolving range of strategies which geographers have adopted over recent decades to organise fieldwork. The fieldwork purposes and opportunities particular to working in the local environment are identified and developed in Chapter 3. A review of the ways in which the use of information and communications technology (ICT) can enhance local fieldwork is provided in Chapter 4. Chapter 5 covers the organisation and management and health and safety aspects of local fieldwork.

Part Two presents some more recently developed examples of local fieldwork practice. Here the emphasis is on new ideas and fresh applications of established field practices. We do not intend to include all field environments or areas of the syllabus, nor do we advocate that the activities presented in Part Two should replace the excellent fieldwork approaches which geography departments have developed over the years. In our experience many departments have established the resources to enable students to investigate a range of topics - often in the local environment. Many schools undertake surveys of urban land-use, industrial location, traffic, residential areas and environmental quality, retail patterns, river work, rural land-use and recreation and tourism. However, some less familiar themes are presented here to offer new ideas to complement, and in some cases extend, this established work.

Where detailed methodologies are suggested, they will need to be adapted to the circumstances of your school locality and the fieldwork policies of your school. Through these examples we explore the role of ICT in local fieldwork, covering both the more familiar use of spreadsheets to tabulate, chart and analyse data and the growing possibilities of integrating secondary data (sourced from websites) with the students' primary field data. Chapter 6 offers ways of introducing the locale to students through experiential trails and mapping skills. The sections on 'Infiltration' and 'Roof hydrographs' in Chapter 7 re-examine the use of the immediate surroundings of the school for learning about hydrology. Chapter 8 relates first-hand studies of weather and climate to secondary data gathered using ICT skills. Both chapters include established practice and newer methods.

The potential integration of local fieldwork, the geography curriculum and aspects of environmental education and the sustainability agenda is explored in the context of renewable energy, air pollution, transport futures and food miles in Chapters 9, 10 and 11. Chapter 12 reviews novel activities linking fieldwork in biogeography to ideas about multiculturalism.

Part One

Purposes, strategies, opportunities and practice

This section overviews the purposes, strategies and practice of local fieldwork. It also discusses the opportunities offered by working in the local environment

Chapter 1

Fieldwork: a range of purposes

As teachers of geography most of us have a number of purposes in mind when we organise and undertake fieldwork with students. These purposes may focus primarily on activities which support the national curriculum through developing geographical knowledge, understanding and skills, but often extend to less tangible purposes concerning aesthetic appreciations, values education, wider vocational skills and the social and personal development of individual students. Figure 1 summarises some of these purposes and provides examples of specific fieldwork objectives. This summary is based on educational literature and workshops with practising teachers; it is not intended to be a comprehensive review.

Clearly, the priorities which we attach to the purposes of fieldwork will influence our strategy. These include:

- the roles of teacher and students,
- the focus of study,
- the chosen location,
- the methods used to collect data, and
- the sorts of experiences students have during the fieldwork.

Within each geography department different teachers may attach different priorities to fieldwork. Our view of fieldwork is strongly influenced by our perspective on the role of education as a whole and is, therefore, imbued with our personal values. Voicing and recognising individual priorities may be helpful before organising the fieldwork. Figure 1 could provide the starting point for such a discussion: for example, by identifying which fieldwork purposes have been omitted. This sort of framework may also help you to justify fieldwork to colleagues in other departments, to the school management team or to parents. Spending some time considering the purposes of fieldwork will help you promote fieldwork as a means of achieving a whole range of educational purposes. In this context fieldwork can be seen as:

- a successful way of supporting the geography national curriculum and in motivating students,
- a focus for cross-curricular themes and a means of forging links with other areas of the curriculum,
- a practical way of providing training in vocationally relevant skills, and
- contributing to students' personal development, social skills and ecological and political literacy.

Figure 1: A summary of fieldwork purposes identified by geography practitioners.

Broad educational purpose	Related fieldwork aim	Examples of specific fieldwork objectives
Conceptual (knowledge and understanding)	Supporting the geography curriculum through promoting geographical knowledge and understanding	• Reinforcing geographical terminology through tangible examples • Identifying and defining geographical questions, issues and problems • Understanding relationships between sets of geographical factors • Understanding the processes underlying geographical patterns in space and time
Skills related	Developing organisational and technical aptitudes relevant to both geography and the world of work	• Planning a geographical investigation or enquiry • Developing geographical skills which can be transferred to individual enquiries, coursework and employment • Practising and applying technical skills (including ICT) in a real world context • Developing skills in locating, retrieving, analysing and interpreting information
Aesthetic	Developing sensitivity to and appreciation of landscapes and the built and natural environment	• Developing a sense of place • Developing an ability to 'read' a landscape • Encouraging emotional responses to environments • Expressing preferences about environments • Recording and interpreting the experience of landscape through creative activity
Values related	Developing awareness of a range of viewpoints in relation to social, political and ecological concerns	• Recognising and respecting the values of others • Clarifying and justifying personal values • Seeing the wider social and ecological effects of changes in the environment
Social and personal development	Promoting self-confidence and an ability to work co-operatively	• Developing co-operation and communication skills through participating in group work • Encouraging a sense of adventure • Building confidence and resilience through offering challenges • Promoting camaraderie and social fusion through participation in a common endeavour

The case studies in Part Two have been assembled with all of these intentions in mind.

In our experience some fieldwork aims and objectives can be fully explored within the school locality while others are more readily achieved in contrasting environments or through residential fieldwork. By promoting the benefits of local fieldwork you may inadvertently undermine the case for residential fieldwork or day visits away from the school locality. A clear distinction should be made between the two endeavours by pointing out that each approach has distinct and different educational purpose. For example, opportunities to develop students' understanding of certain concepts in physical geography may require access to more natural environments than those immediately accessible to schools in urban areas. In addition, aspects of a student's development of social aptitudes and aesthetic sensibilities may be more readily achieved in a residential setting, perhaps with access to remote rural areas. You can argue, however, that there are specific strengths associated with fieldwork in the school locality. Chapter 2 is aimed at helping you review the full range of fieldwork strategies before you detail the particular opportunities created by organising fieldwork locally.

Fieldwork:
a range of strategies

Over recent decades the approaches to fieldwork adopted by teachers of geography have evolved in response to the shifts in geographical thinking and as a result of changes in educational practice. The move from didactic styles of teaching towards more student-centred ways of learning has been followed, in some quarters, by a return to more traditional teaching methods.

The key change in geographical thinking during the 1960s involved a rapid move away from descriptive approaches (which were characterised by synthesis and an emphasis on regional identity) towards systematic studies using the quantitative tools of science, hypothesis testing, statistical analysis and the search for theory. The lack of synthesis and purpose in some of this (highly quantitative) work has since led to an interest in the application of geographical knowledge to real world problems - particularly in physical geography. This trend is reinforced by a growing awareness of various environmental crises. Changing approaches to fieldwork mirror, but to some extent lag behind, the shifts in geographical thinking.

By identifying a range of fieldwork strategies we do not imply that a particular approach is to be preferred or promoted; rather we recognise that each fulfils rather different purposes. The best fieldwork teachers have an awareness of the full range of strategies and a clear view of the purposes of the fieldwork and can vary their approach according to the needs of students and the available environments. The variety of approaches we offer are not mutually exclusive and several of the frameworks for organising local fieldwork draw together elements from a number of available strategies.

Figure 2 provides a summary of the strategies and purposes of local fieldwork (some of which may be more familiar than others). Examples of appropriate fieldwork activities are shown in the final column. Fuller reviews of a range of fieldwork strategies are available in a number of other sources (see, for example, Job, 1996, 1999).

The field excursion

The traditional field excursion may be a familiar format to many geography teachers from either school or undergraduate days (some geography departments in higher education still use the formal lecture approach in the field). In this

Strategy	Purposes	Characteristic activities
The traditional field excursion	• Developing skills in geographical recording and interpretation • Showing relationships between physical and human landscape features • Developing concept of landscape evolving over time • Developing an appreciation of landscape and nurturing a sense of place	Students guided through a landscape by teacher with local knowledge, often following a route on a large scale map. Sites grid-referenced and described with aid of landscape sketches and sketch maps to explore the underlying geology, topographical features, the mantle of soil and vegetation and the landscape history in terms of human activity. Students listen, record and answer questions concerning possible interpretations of the landscape.
Field research based on hypothesis testing	• Applying geographical theory or generalised models to real world situations • Generating and applying hypotheses based on theory to be tested through collections of appropriate field data • Developing skills in analysing data using statistical methods in order to test field situations against geographical theory	The conventional deductive approach involves initial consideration of geographical theory, leading to the formulation of hypotheses which are then tested against field situations through the collection of quantitative data and testing against expected patterns and relationships. More flexible variants of this approach encourage students to develop their own hypotheses based on initial field observations, thereby incorporating an inductive element.
Geographical enquiry	• Encouraging students to identify, construct and ask geographical questions • Enabling students to identify and gather relevant information to answer geographical questions and offer explanations and interpretations of their findings • Enabling students to apply their findings to the wider world and personal decisions	A geographical question, issue or problem is identified, ideally from student's own experiences in the field. Students are then supported in the gathering of appropriate data (quantitative or qualitative) to answer their key question. Findings are evaluated and the implications applied to the wider world and personal decisions where appropriate.
Discovery fieldwork	• Allowing students to discover their own interests in a landscape (rather than through a teacher) • Allowing students to develop their own focus of study and methods of investigation • Encouraging self-confidence and self-motivation by putting students in control of their learning	Teacher assumes the role of animateur, allowing the group to follow its own route through the landscape. When students ask questions these are countered with further questions to encourage deeper thinking. A discussion and recording session then identifies themes for further investigation in small groups. This further work has arisen from students' perceptions and preferences rather than those of teachers.
Sensory fieldwork	• Encouraging new sensitivities to environments through using all the senses • Nurturing caring attitudes to nature and empathy with other people through emotional engagement • Acknowledging that sensory experience is as valid as intellectual activity in understanding our surroundings	Structured activities designed to stimulate the senses in order to promote awareness of environments. Sensory walks, use of blindfolds, sound maps, poetry and artwork are characteristic activities. Can be used as an introductory activity prior to more conventional investigative work or to develop a sense of place, aesthetic appreciation or critical appraisal of environmental change.

Figure 2: Fieldwork strategies and purposes.

situation your students adopt a relatively passive role; you are seen as the all-knowing provider of knowledge; and the landscape is interpreted uncritically - as if it is devoid of environmental, social or political conflict. It is easy to criticise this approach from today's viewpoint of how learning ought to take place; however, those of you who have experienced this type of fieldwork may recall the pleasure and satisfaction of acquiring the skills to 'read' and interpret a landscape as a whole, and thereby to grasp something of the 'essence' of a place. While there may well be a role for this approach in more distant places, its applicability to work in local fieldwork in urban areas may be limited - not least because of the practical difficulties of talking to a group of students either safely or effectively in an urban environment.

Hypothesis testing

Hypothesis testing and data collection in fieldwork remains a dominant model in fieldwork practice in schools, field centres and in the organisation of individual coursework at all levels. It provides a straightforward, easily-understood framework, where the testing of field data against models or expected trends culminates in a clear end-point. However, research into the outcomes of using rigidly hypothesis-based fieldwork has provided convincing criticisms of this approach. Harvey (1991), has identified a number of shortcomings of adopting this approach at A-level some of which may be equally applicable to fieldwork at key stage 3 and GCSE.

1   Focus of studies pre-determined by teachers rather than arising from students' own field experiences and perceptions.

2   Tension of purpose between thorough and clear treatment of concepts and equipping students with the skills to carry out independent investigation.

3   Dependency of conceptual understanding on processed data rather than direct field experiences.

4   Weak links between observations in the field and subsequent data processing.

5   Opportunities for transferring field experiences into examination answers were often missed.

6   Environmental decisions considered only in the light of objective and neutral facts emerging from hypothesis testing with limited discussion of different values positions.

7   Lack of integration of sub-systems/themes into a holistic view.
    (Harvey, 1991, pp. 440-64)

There was an overall sense that the involvement of students in data collection and analysis alone was not achieving the full range of purposes that fieldwork has the potential to fulfil (Harvey, 1991). The more student-centred approach associated with geographical enquiry addresses, to some extent, many of Harvey's criticisms. Nowadays enquiry-based fieldwork often incorporates hypothesis testing into a more open-ended framework. There are good arguments for retaining hypothesis-based investigation as part of a repertoire of locally-based fieldwork - not least because some examining boards expect coursework to be structured around the testing of a hypothesis. The fieldwork activities outlined in Chapter 7 (pages 41-47) are appropriate to the construction and testing of hypotheses.

Geographical enquiry

One consequence of the criticism of overly-prescriptive hypothesis testing is that much geography fieldwork is now enquiry-based. This approach is particularly appropriate to the organisation of locally-based fieldwork for a number of reasons.

1 Students have some prior knowledge and experience of their locality. This can contribute to the initial formulation of geographical questions, issues or problems as the basis for fieldwork.

2 The role of values in decisions concerning the environment is more readily appreciated when students are already familiar with the communities and cultures concerned.

3 Where the issues and problems investigated have local immediacy students can apply their findings to personal decision-making.

Enquiry is also appropriate where small groups of students are able to work semi-independently, with each group contributing information to a broader picture. The work on 'Food miles' (pages 71-73), where the investigation involves a range of values positions and possible personal decisions, is particularly appropriate to an enquiry approach.

Discovery learning

'Discovery learning' is a wholly open-ended approach which allows students to find their own points of interest in the landscape. Basing their work on what they rather than you (the teacher) deem important and interesting, the students then develop and extend their investigative work. Legitimate concerns about this approach focus on the possibility of students 'homing in' on themes which have a limited connection to the curriculum. Behavioural and safety problems may also arise simply because fewer of the usual structures and boundaries necessary during fieldwork are in operation.

An example which incorporates some elements of discovery learning within the necessary constraints of safety and fieldwork organisation is presented in Chapter 6 (pages 35-39). In this approach a structured activity can lead to students identifying their own geographical questions from experiences in the local environment.

Sensory fieldwork

'Sensory fieldwork' activities are most often aimed at re-establishing the somewhat fractured connections between people and nature. So they are often seen as most applicable in more natural or remote wilderness environments, i.e. accessible on residential field visits. Van Matre's programmes of Earth education emphasise sensory experiences as pathways to understanding environments and our place within them. This approach can be summarised by the following extract from Van Matre's work:

> 'We feared entrapment by the idea that things are only real if they can be measured. Many of life's most rewarding, enriching and heartfelt experiences can barely be put into words, let alone placed on a scale. If we relied too much on the usual processes of collecting and testing, what would happen to our goals of instilling a sense of wonder, a sense of place and a reverence for life? If we failed to develop appreciations in our haste to convey understandings, if we overemphasised analytical skills at the expense of deep natural experiences, what would we gain - people who could take life apart, but cared nothing for keeping it together?' (Van Matre, 1979, p. xviii).

Such thinking may appear more appropriate for biology and ecology and the experience of wilderness than for local geography fieldwork based in a more managed and sub-urbanised environment. However, it has been proposed that if the purpose of fieldwork encompasses the promotion of 'caring' and 'change for a better world' then engagement of the emotions and senses may be as important as the application of rational and analytical thinking.

Figure 3: An integrated model for outdoor education. Source: Hawkins, 1987.

Awareness/Acclimatisation
Activities to heighten awareness based on personal experience of an environment, involving sharpening of perceptions, development of critical visual analysis and communicating personal responses

Learners discover their own route into the environment by finding a personal point of contact

Investigation
Participants identify a focus for further investigation then carry out individual or group enquiry to further knowledge and understanding

Concern/Action
Development of feelings of personal responsibility for an environment and a desire to participate in decisions which affect it

Figure 3 is based on a scheme put forward by Hawkins (1987). This integrates elements of several different strategies: aspects of discovery and sensory experience are introduced as student-centred starting points, which lead into a core of largely enquiry-based investigation. The outcomes of the investigative phase feed through into a further phase. It is within this phase that students consider their work in terms of personal decisions or involvement in decisions concerning the environments they have studied. The continuity implied in Figure 3 is very appropriate for work in the home locality where fieldwork can be linked to experiences both before and after the investigative phase.

We believe that much established fieldwork practice is pertinent to the core of Hawkins' (1987) model, but the 'Acclimatisation' and 'Concern/Action' phases are perhaps less familiar. Chapter 3 considers how the organisation of local fieldwork enables elements of this model to be put into practice. In addition, several of the case studies in Part Two include schemes of work (see Chapters 9, 10 and 11) which can lead into the areas of 'Concern' and 'Action' shown in Figure 3.

Opportunities from working locally

When selecting appropriate strategies for local fieldwork it is helpful to identify those purposes which are *better* achieved or can *only* be achieved through local fieldwork. Equally in planning (and justifying) more distant fieldwork, it is useful to be able to refer to those purposes which are not readily met through work in the local environment.

Referring back to Figure 1 there are relatively few fieldwork purposes which cannot normally be attempted through local fieldwork. Working locally also offers certain important opportunities, which are less evident when we undertake fieldwork in more distant locations.

Start with student perceptions

The first of these opportunities relates to the potential to re-visit sites on a number of occasions, a pre-requisite if we are interested in the sort of progression which can be achieved. Using Hawkins' (1987) outdoor experience model (Figure 3), the initial phase of 'Acclimatisation' may seem daunting because it appears to lack the necessary structure to maintain order while considering safety and attaining purposeful work. The prospect of releasing students into the local environment to 'see what's there' without a framework or boundaries would be asking for trouble. It might also limit the outcomes in terms of geographical experience. On page 36 we propose a framework of activities which will allow students to look beneath the surface of their surroundings and generate their own geographical questions. These can then lead into more tangible investigations and enquiries. The key elements of this Acclimatisation process are that:

- students have identified their own questions and concerns, in part from field experience, and
- students feel personally involved in their field environment and may develop a personal concern for its wellbeing.

Caring attitudes may be a pre-requisite to involvement in the community to promote change and improvement - surely a key element of active citizenship.

Fieldwork and sustainability issues

A major element of the framework for outdoor activity put forward by Hawkins (1987) is that the investigation or enquiry phase ceases to be an end in itself. Students are encouraged to apply the knowledge, understanding and insights they acquire during the activity to problems, issues and concerns in the locality. Many enquiry topics in the school locality lend themselves to encouraging students to apply their findings - both in terms of personal decision making and getting involved in influencing policy decisions. Some enquiries, such as investigation of traffic (Chapter 10), and food miles (Chapter 11), allow findings to be related to both local and global contexts.

Geography plays a major role in raising the environmental awareness of students, particularly in terms of global issues. Climate change, pollution, inequality, population and resource imbalance and habitat destruction are all issues covered in geography lessons. In our experience students demonstrate a variety of responses to such challenges - considerable anxiety is a common reaction in many individuals, while for others detachment, negation or apathy are characteristic responses. For some students environmental and social concerns simply add to their burden of worries and insecurities - an unsatisfactory, yet unsurprising, situation. The geography national curriculum frequently raises issues and problems that seem beyond our control without necessarily helping students to make the connections between those problems and their everyday lives and immediate surroundings. Yet here, perhaps, lies the greatest potential for local fieldwork: we can use it to take a critical look at our surroundings - from the energy use in the school buildings (Chapter 9) and how students and teachers travel to school (Chapter 10) to the origin of food on the supermarket shelf (Chapter 11). The information students gather can help them forge the vital links between here and now and distant places and the future.

Without support and guidance, many students may feel that they have neither the right nor the ability to influence policies and change in their localities. There are, however, a growing number of initiatives whereby students can articulate concerns which have arisen (or been highlighted) by enquiry work in their locality. Whole-school approaches to the greening of the school premises are becoming commonplace, often with students taking a co-ordinating role. In addition, involvement of schools in local authority policies through the 'Local Agenda 21' process can carry the principles of sustainable development from the geography lesson out into the community. While healthy debate continues over the meaning of sustainability and sustainable development, there is agreement that education for sustainability has three closely related elements:

1 **Awareness**: I have the knowledge and understanding to recognise the need for change.

2 **Empowerment**: I have the self-esteem and motivation to influence change.

3 **Commitment**: I will act.
   (Cooper, 1999, pp. 37-40).

Geography and locally-based fieldwork in particular have great potential to develop the initial awareness of issues, concerns and problems in our localities. Moreover, through fieldwork activities geography can often contribute indirectly to a student's self-esteem and motivation. Certainly by concerning itself with how decisions are made, geography can contribute to an understanding of how change can occur. However, if we are interested in the more far-reaching intentions of education for sustainability, then whole-school and whole-curriculum involvement is necessary. Ideally this takes place in the context of the local community: establishing links between the school, the community and Local Agenda 21 activities is proving a practical way forward in a number of schools. Several thought-provoking explorations of this broader educational endeavour are available (see Orr, 1994; Cooper, 1999).

Time – the extra dimension

One highly significant opportunity which working locally offers is the incorporation of change over time into students' experiences. In many areas of geography the appreciation of spatial variation presents only half the picture. Indeed, in the case of some geographical systems, the understandings that come from temporal change may have greater significance than spatial change.

Over the few hectares which make up the school locality many phenomena show far greater change through time than from place to place. Some of the more dramatic differences and intriguing stories are to be found in:

- the day to day vagaries and the seasonal rhythms of weather,
- the diurnal flows of traffic, goods and people,
- the longer term changes in the vigour of local economies, and
- the incursion of vegetation onto derelict land.

Working locally enables students to sense and record the short-term changes. While, with careful record keeping, storage of past data and organisation of resources, students can have access to 'snapshots' from the past. (Increasingly ICT offers opportunities for storing information and images in digital form and, through the use of databases, students can help catalogue information stored in box files, filing cabinets, map chests, slide collections and video libraries for future reference.) The 'snapshots' may be literal and visual or in the form of maps at various dates, data gathered by past students, written or tape-recorded recollections of older members of the community. These resources should help demonstrate how and why places change.

The time dimension is relevant to geographical understanding as well as contributing to the student's developing relationship with their locality. The act of participating in the continuity of life in the school neighbourhood helps to engender a sense of place, a sense of belonging and feelings of responsibility for the future wellbeing of the locality.

Chapter 4

Integrating local fieldwork with ICT

Integrating ICT with fieldwork offers students the opportunity to develop and apply the full range of ICT skills. In addition to the established practices of word-processing text and using spreadsheets to record, analyse and present quantitative data, there are growing opportunities for students to integrate information from CD-Roms and websites and to incorporate digitally-processed images from scanners and digital cameras in their fieldwork reports.

Integrating ICT with quantitative fieldwork investigations greatly reduces the time taken up by 'number crunching' sets of data. While quantitative fieldwork often generated large data sets which were tabulated on the board, students now use more manageable spreadsheets. Spreadsheets can be set up on a network of computers to allow each fieldwork group to simultaneously input their 'row' of data and thus contribute to a common data set on which the whole class can then work. This sort of application obviates many of the problems associated with manually collating and analysing data; a task which was often so demanding that little enthusiasm was left to explore the geographical concepts and relationships.

Word processing

While no student should be discouraged from submitting a well-presented hand-written report with hand-drawn maps and charts, ICT will help those who prefer to produce professional quality word-processed reports with printed charts, scanned maps and diagrams and digitally-processed images. You should point out that, whether hand-written or word-processed, good work requires the same standards of care. Careless use of ICT can, and sadly does, result in poorly-presented write-ups (usually through a failure to carefully read through and edit reports) which detracts from otherwise good work. Encourage your students to check spelling and grammar in the text and the scales, labelling and legends on charts in all their work. Emphasise that word-processing packages offer them the opportunity to edit and re-work material without starting from scratch.

Much word-processing software is now designed as a presentation package. Students can import tables, charts, maps and images into text from other packages much more easily. This gives a more cohesive overall appearance.

Spreadsheets

The widespread development of spreadsheet templates for the analysis of fieldwork data has now greatly reduced the 'number crunching' effort. This means students can devote more time to the interpretation of fieldwork findings. There are, however, a number of issues to consider if the use of spreadsheets in fieldwork is to support successful learning. These include the way students record information in the field, the use of commercially-produced or school-made spreadsheets and the storage and retrieval of data - each of which is dealt with separately below.

Field recording

It is tempting to extend the use of hardware into the field by equipping students with lap-top or palm-top computers which will enable them to record data directly onto a pre-prepared spreadsheet. This appears attractive in terms of using compact versions of computer technology to their full potential. In practice it may be constrained by a number of factors:

- Insufficient machines to equip all fieldwork groups.
- Few of the machines are fully weatherproof.
- Insufficient supervision resulting in some data loss.
- In some urban areas students may be at risk of assault (from thieves) if they are carrying valuable electronic equipment.

For these reasons it is probably more satisfactory to issue students with field recording sheets based on print-outs of the spreadsheet. Ensuring that these sheets have the same layout and format as the spreadsheet will greatly assist data entry. In addition, you should make a clear distinction between cells which contain calculations (and are not for field data) and those which are for students to insert their data. Retain all 'hard copies' (printouts) of field recording sheets even after data entry in order to check any rogue values.

Commercial software or DIY spreadsheets?

There are several commercially-available software packages available for the analysis of field data (e.g. river channel data, slope data). These will already have the calculations and graphics set up and may include statistical analyses (for suggestions on suitable packages, see St John and Richardson, 1996, 1997). You should ensure that the ones you choose are compatible with the specific field methods, units, numbers of sites and range of variables you plan to use. Alternatively, students can use school-produced spreadsheets. Prior to quantitative fieldwork, geography and/or IT staff can work with students to create their own spreadsheets. This kind of approach allows for:

- the development of ICT skills in a real world context,
- the production of a tailor-made spreadsheet with labelled rows and columns specific to the methods and field locations,
- the introduction of differentiation (with tasks involving visual interpretation of charts and graphs aimed at less able students and tasks where more able students can utilise their higher level skills to analyse the statistics), and
- comparisons to be made between different forms of graphical presentation.

Data storage and retrieval

Many local fieldwork activities are concerned with analysing spatial variations. The use of spreadsheets enables past data to be stored and retrieved, introducing the possibility of analysing and comparing temporal variation and trends. Groups of students can repeat a survey at different times of year or compare their data to sets collected during previous years. Microclimate and river data are particularly appropriate for the study of seasonal variations, while traffic or land-use data may show interesting longer-term variations. To ensure that comparisons are valid the sites and methods of collection must be reasonably similar.

Image processing using ICT

Digital cameras enable photographic images to be electronically processed for inclusion in write-ups, coursework and displays at a faster and cheaper rate than scans of prints from conventional still cameras. To make full use of such images, students can be encouraged to carry out annotated field sketches of each recorded image. Back in the classroom the students can superimpose annotations and titles from their sketches over digitally imposed images which can then be inserted into the text of fieldwork reports. This avoids the misconception that photography (conventional or digital) is a substitute for field sketching as a means of recording and interpreting the landscape.

Photographs taken with a still camera can be scanned and incorporated into fieldwork write-ups. Images or charts can be printed onto printer-compatible overhead transparency sheets for use either in follow-up work or presentations by students.

Secondary data

There is increasing scope to integrate primary data from fieldwork with secondary data which has been downloaded from either CD-Roms or websites. This approach can allow:

- sophisticated data from secondary sources (often gathered using costly equipment) to be compared to primary data collected using simpler and more affordable methods,
- aspects of the locality to be set in a regional, national or global context, and
- for the presentation of data from primary sources to be compared with past data from secondary sources.

Figure 4 outlines a number of examples where secondary data can add an extra dimension to the interpretation of field results.

Primary data from local fieldwork	Secondary data from CD-Rom, website or floppy disk
Environmental quality	Small area (wards or enumeration districts) socio-economic data from census records on CD-Rom
Local measurements of windspeed, wind direction, atmospheric pressure or traffic data	Local air pollution data downloaded from DETR air pollution website (www.detr.gov.uk)
Daily weather readings	Satellite image and weather maps from MetFAX or Met Office website (www.met-office.gov.uk)
Rainfall, infiltration, interception data	River discharge data from the Environment Agency website (www.environment-agency.gov.uk)

Figure 4: Integration of field data with information from secondary sources.

School websites and e-mail

The results of fieldwork activities are very appropriate materials for incorporation into school websites. Establishing connections with schools in contrasting places can involve the exchange of local fieldwork results and images. This can take place either via school websites or as e-mail attachments.

Provided the schools exchanging information have used similar fieldwork methods there are enormous possibilities for students to compare the school locality with those in distant places - particularly where international links can be established. A number of organisations promote school links through websites and e-mail. These include local authorities, some internet service providers, the British Council (www.wotw.org.uk/) and the Virtual Teacher Centre (vtc.ngfl.gov. uk/resource/cits/geog/emailpart.html) (Burn, 1999, p. 149). The exchange of digitally-processed images of the school locality via e-mail offers opportunities for exciting geographical work.

Chapter 5

Organisation and management

In planning local fieldwork it is helpful to consider both the fieldwork activity itself and organisational aspects in terms of school policy and liaison with colleagues, parents and school management. These two areas of planning are often interdependent and it may be necessary to adapt fieldwork activities in the light of school policies on safety and supervision or as a result of a hazard appraisal.

Working locally generally avoids the time-consuming tasks and problems associated with organising day visits or residential fieldwork (e.g. collecting money from students, organising transport and dealing with other institutions/agencies). If the activity can be accomplished within the school premises then even the need to obtain parental consent can normally be avoided.

Safety and risk assessment

Safety is of over-riding importance in any fieldwork activity. You must first ensure that the activity and the level of supervision comply with school policy. You will also need to carry out some form of site hazard or risk assessment. This assessment should consider the journey to the site(s) as well as the actual location(s) where the students will work. Figure 5 provides a checklist of factors to consider in a typical urban situation with close proximity to the school. It should help you to assess and minimise the potential hazards. Your own hazard assessment should also follow five stages:

Stage 1: Visit all fieldwork sites and assess the access to each one. Consider all possible hazards given the nature of the fieldwork environment, the activity and variations with weather, the season, the time of day and the characteristics of the students involved.

Stage 2: Consider who could be harmed and how they might be harmed in each location.

Stage 3: Evaluate the risk from the hazard - Can it be removed or controlled? - where this is not possible be prepared to alter the location, route, timing or activity.

Stage 4: Record the results of your hazard assessment and make notes for your pre-fieldwork briefings.

Stage 5: Review and revise the assessment as necessary each time the fieldwork is carried out.

Feed the findings of this assessment into specific items for your pre-fieldwork briefings - both to students and adult helpers.

You should also consider the route - some of the greatest risks may occur travelling to and from fieldwork sites, for example, crossing roads and, if transport is being used, getting in and out of minibuses or coaches. Lunch/drinks/toilet breaks, possibly between each fieldwork activity, must be built into the timetable. Appropriate boundaries to behaviour during these times should also be clearly established.

Figure 5: Potential hazards in an urban setting and ways to minimise them.

	Potential hazard	Minimising hazard
Traffic	Crossing roads Walking off pavements onto the road	Avoid crossing busy roads. Use pelican/zebra crossings wherever possible. Brief students of any specific traffic hazards, e.g. bus lanes, bends with limited visibility. Ensure students stay on pavements. Wherever possible avoid walking as a large group along roads without pavements or verges.
Pavements	Students obstructing other pedestrians when carrying out activities Obstructions, such as scaffolding against a building	Brief students to think about where they are standing: • to carry out their work, and • in relation to obstructions. Ensure groups of students stand where the pavement is wide enough to accommodate everyone and allow the general public to pass by.
Students	Students become separated from the working group	Brief students to always stay with their working group. Have a responsible adult as a 'back marker' if walking in a large group. Brief students to return to or contact school immediately they become separated. Ensure every student has school office telephone number and change for the telephone.
Abduction	More of a perceived hazard, but one which often causes most concern when activities extend beyond school premises	Maintain a minimum group size of three students and ensure that groups stay together. Wherever possible ensure each group is working within sight of an adult helper.
Conflict	Aggression from members of the public	Brief students to show courtesy and to seek assistance or walk away from potential conflict. Ensure students are able to simply explain what they are doing if approached by members of the public. Supply them with an explanatory note on the school letterheaded paper if necessary.

Pre-fieldwork briefing

Effective pre-fieldwork briefing is the key to both successful and safe fieldwork. Separate briefings can cover the purpose and detail of the fieldwork activity and safety matters. Make specific reference to any perceived hazards at the fieldwork site and how the students and adult helpers can minimise any potential dangers. Some briefings can take place in the classroom, while others are more appropriate on-site. However, where students are to work in small groups with a minimum of supervision, all pre-fieldwork briefings should take place before leaving school. This approach is important for urban fieldwork as it is difficult to gather the whole class safely in one place and make yourself heard.

Two particular issues which deserve special mention during pre-fieldwork briefings are unforeseen problems/emergencies and the use of mobile telephones or personal stereos. Clear information on these issues will help students to minimise the risk to themselves during the fieldwork.

Unforeseen problems/emergencies: In case unforeseen problems do arise while off the school premises students should carry the school office telephone number and have change for the telephone. Ensure that the school office staff are aware of the exact location(s) and nature of the fieldwork and know who to contact in an emergency.

In the event of an accident, assault or abduction (attempted or otherwise) students away from immediate supervision should be instructed to contact the emergency services in the first instance, then the school.

Personal stereos/mobile telephones: It is particularly inappropriate for students to have personal stereos or mobile telephones with them during fieldwork. These pieces of equipment distract students from the fieldwork task and can prevent them hearing important instructions or safety information. The use of personal stereos and mobile telephones can also create a communication barriers within the fieldwork group and will isolate individuals from the sounds of the environment.

Group work and supervision

There is considerable benefit to be gained from organising local fieldwork on the basis of small groups of students working semi-independently. The difficulties of keeping a large group of students together, addressing the group in noisy streets, obstructing pavements and attracting unwelcome attention from passers-by can be overcome through small group work. The benefits of this approach include:

- greater student autonomy and responsibility for the fieldwork,
- the ability to gather more varied sets of information contemporaneously, and
- the sense of cohesion that comes from working in small groups contributing to a common effort.

With appropriate briefing and supervision it is often easier to ensure safety, particularly from traffic hazards, and avoid inconveniencing members of the public. You must, however, consider group work in relation to school policies, particularly the degree of supervision required during school time. Where it is practicable to do so, involving suitably briefed and responsible year 12 and 13 students in the supervision of small groups of younger students on local fieldwork will benefit both the older and the younger students. Other sources of supervision include colleagues, support staff, parents and school governors. A thorough briefing of everyone involved in supervision is vital and it needs to include attention to both the field activities and the safety matters.

Field recording

The following points may be helpful in the practical organisation of effective recording of field information.

1 If there are several maps, recording or briefing sheets staple or bind them together to reduce the possibility of them being dropped or blown away.

2 Include a title or cover page with space for the student's name and teaching group, so that the worksheets can be easily collected and sorted at the end of the fieldwork.

3 State the aims of the fieldwork clearly so that the students and helpers understand the purpose of the activity.

4 Number each sheet and number or letter each section clearly to help the students find the correct place quickly in the field.

5 Clearly indicate the difference between guidance notes and questions on the worksheets. Use easy to understand language for the guidance notes, e.g. 'draw' and 'measure'.

6 A clipboard is ideal to rest on, but an A4 piece of hardboard with two rubber bands is an inexpensive alternative. A clear plastic bag large enough to cover both the worksheets and the clipboard and for the student to hold a pencil/pen inside will enable them to carry on recording even in wet weather.

7 The recording of information can be greatly assisted by providing some of the following:

- an outline or part-drawn sketch to aid the production of field sketches

- a ready-drawn sketch with loose sticky labels which need to be put in the right places

- an incomplete outline map of the field study area which needs further detail

- a paragraph of text with spaces in which students insert words or phrases

- a checklist of features with boxes which students tick if they observe the feature

- sentences or phrases which could be ringed or underlined.

The worksheet pack should also include plain or lined paper which the students can use for their own observations and the more open-ended tasks you set.

Planning follow-up

In order to ensure that students, colleagues, school management and parents see local fieldwork as a purposeful and worthwhile undertaking it is vital that sufficient time is allocated to effective follow-up.

It is helpful for students if you make a distinction between the recording, analysis and interpretation of fieldwork findings, but they should also see the three tasks as integrated. Where quantitative data has been collected and recording has been completed in the field, analysis should begin with some sort of **collation** process. Put simply the information collected in different places or at different times by different fieldwork groups is drawn together to form a common set of results to which all students have access. A spreadsheet will help at this stage.

Once collation is complete the students' preliminary **presentation** of their results using summary tables, percentages, graphs, charts and maps can follow. This stage can involve the use of ICT, so book appropriate computing facilities during the planning stage and ensure that any software packages are both thoroughly tested and ready for use by the students.

The students can then undertake an analysis of the results. Strictly speaking this involves a search for order, pattern and relationships in the data and should lead to explanations. The final stage of **interpretation** is where findings are considered more broadly and related to theory, expectations and the wider world, leading perhaps to suggested changes in policy or personal decisions.

The follow up can lead to a presentation of the fieldwork outcomes, for instance, an illustrated display in the geography classroom or school corridor. Other opportunities for demonstrating the outcomes of the fieldwork include an audio-visual presentation during assembly, a multi-media presentation accessible on the school computer network or website or an item for a local radio station or newspaper. The latter approach is especially pertinent where the fieldwork is topical or relates to concerns in the local community.

Sources of information on organisation and safety

Fuller treatment of organisational and safety issues concerning school based fieldwork is available in *Health and Safety of Students on Educational Visits* (DfEE, 1998), *Outdoor Education, Safety and Good Practice* (NAFSO, 1998a) and *Fieldwork in Action 3: Managing Out-of-classroom Activities* (Thomas and May, 1994). In addition, the NAFSO *Code of Practice* booklet (NAFSO, 1998b), though written with field studies centres in mind, contains much information pertinent to the organisation of school-based fieldwork.

Part Two

Fresh ideas for field-based schemes of work

Many secondary schools have established fieldwork programmes which cover a range of topics. The new ideas presented in this section will complement these programmes

Chapter 6

Starting points

This activity allows students to use some of their own perceptions of their locality to identify geographical questions. It is a response to some of the problems associated with over-prescriptive data collection activities, where the focus of fieldwork is defined by our perceptions of the locality rather than those of students.

During the pre-fieldwork briefing emphasise the need to record responses and detail the normal health and safety guidance for work beyond the school gate.

Aims

- To encourage students to use all their senses in exploring the locality.
- To stimulate perception through focusing activities.
- To allow students to form their own perceptions of the school locality within an organised framework.
- To use the perceptions of the whole class to identify geographical questions, issues or problems in the school locality.

Method

A collection of tasks or questions designed for the exploration of an urban environment is shown in Figure 6. The nature of these tasks and questions will need to be adapted to the specific environment of the locality. While the questions are quite specific, most will allow students to form their own judgements, preferences or speculations. There are few (if any) right answers. The questions shown in Figure 6 are designed to focus students perceptions on themes such as 'change in the locality', 'environmental quality', 'global links' and 'the requirements of people with particular needs'.

The application of these questions/tasks in local fieldwork is flexible. One approach is to stick them onto a set of cards and give sets to each group of three students together with a street map showing a pre-defined route. To encourage a diversity of experiences, different groups can be given different cards (each sealed in a separate envelope) and/or follow different routes. Along the route a new envelope is opened at random (either every 100m or so or at timed intervals) and the group undertakes the task on the card, carefully locating their position on the street map and recording their responses. Alternatively, the tasks can be incorporated into a worksheet or trail with boxes drawn in for responses.

How many different plants can you find during a five-minute walk?	Which of each of the following pairs of words best describes the majority of people around you: tense/relaxed worried/carefree talking/silent	Imagine you have been transported blindfold and left on this spot. On removing your blindfold, what visual, non-verbal clues would tell you: 1 Which country you were in? 2 Which town or city you were in?
Suggest two ways in which people have improved this area and two ways in which people have spoilt this area.	What three things would you most like to preserve in this area? Why?	What three things would you most like to get rid of in this area? Why?
In what ways is energy being used in this area? Where does the energy come from?	What problems might you have following this route if you were: 1 a child of five 2 a wheelchair user 3 a blind person	Are there any sources of pollution in the area around you?
Find your favourite and least favourite building in the street. Make a quick sketch of each one.	What shape is the land underneath all the buildings?	What things can you see around you which link the area with other countries?
Observe the street around you over the next five minutes. Describe three things which happen (write them down).	Find a safe place to stop out of the way of traffic and other people. Close your eyes and listen. 1 What is the first sound you notice? 2 What is the second sound you notice?	Choose three words which might help to describe this area to someone who has never been here.
What are the three main colours in the street in front of you?	Imagine you are homeless and find a place nearby where you might attempt to spend the night.	How many trees can you see from where you are standing?

Figure 6: Starting points for exploring an urban setting.

Follow-up

The follow-up to this activity involves a 'report back' session of all the experiences and perceptions. Appoint a scribe to record the experiences of the whole class on the board. Though prompted (and to some extent controlled by the nature of the tasks and questions on the cards) the outcome is a collection of perceptions of the school locality based on the students' own interpretations and judgements. Compare this approach to the traditional field excursion described on pages 13-14.

The second stage is to group the experiences into themes. These might be under headings such as 'traffic', 'shops', 'people', 'buildings', 'nature' and 'pollution' or for older students, themes such as 'change', 'conflict' or 'problems'. Another classification which has been used for grouping a diversity of perceptions, is the simple and memorable ... 'the good', 'the bad' and 'the ugly'!

This 'inventory of experiences' can then lead to the identification of geographical questions, issues or problems which form the basis of a more formal geographical enquiry.

Map skills and orienteering

Orienteering within the school grounds offers students the opportunity to develop a range of map skills. These can start with orientation of a map and lead on to relating maps to the landscape, following bearings and gaining familiarity with map scales. Skills learnt in the school grounds can be practised on field trips away from the school locality and will provide a grounding for those students who participate in the Duke of Edinburgh Award Scheme. Orienteering is also an enjoyable activity for students who are about to or have recently started at secondary school and can readily be included in their induction day.

Aims

- To develop a range of map skills.
- To enable new students to orientate themselves in a new environment.

Method

A good up-to-date large-scale base map of the school grounds is important. Depending on the extent of the school grounds this could be enlarged on the photocopier from a 1:2500 or 1:1250 plan to give a convenient scale of 1:1000 or 1:500 (but check your school is covered to copy maps). Check the school files: there may well be a suitable plan already in use for administrative or maintenance purposes or you can obtain school-centred plans through your LEA or local Ordnance Survey agent. Using these resources your students can develop a variety of map skills through a number of activities.

Orientation

Set up twelve or so control points, each with either a hole punch, a coloured marker pen or a letter firmly attached to an immovable object. Students first orientate the map to north and you can point out key features. Groups of two or three students visit each control point and record evidence that they have been there. Stagger the start times to reduce the possibility of groups simply following each other.

Introducing map scales

Identify two points on the map 100m apart with no intervening obstructions. Students measure the distance on the map in millimetres, relate this to the map scale, walk the distance between the two points on the ground and count the number of paces. The connection between distance in metres, map distance in millimetres and paced distance on the ground is thus established. Each student can then work out their average pace length in metres.

Bearings

If a sufficient number of compasses are available students can first practice finding the directions of a series of bearings in the classroom. Check that the map of the school has north to south grid lines, then send students outside to practise taking a series of bearings. These should be between two points taken from the map and the students should use the compass to establish the direction of travel on the ground.

These three skills will enable students to attempt a fuller orienteering course.

Orienteering

A progression in orienteering skills can begin with a course set out as a series of instructions (without a map) such as:

1 'From the main door of the school walk for 25 paces on a bearing of 90 degrees to control point 1'

2 'From control 1 take 50 paces on a bearing of 190 degrees to control point 2' and so on.

At each control point the students must either mark a card or record some information to show they have found it. Think of a short geographical word, phrase or even an anagram and mark each control point with one or two letters from it. You can use this to quickly double-check the success of each group.

The next stage is to provide students with a map showing a numbered sequence of control points which have to be located by:

1 taking a bearing from the map using the compass,

2 establishing the approximate distance in metres or paces, and

3 following the bearing for the required distance to locate the control point.

Extension

Students can set up their own orienteering course within the school grounds as a series of bearings and distances either on the ground or on a map. Other students then have to follow the course.

If a safe area of open country is accessible from school use the methods described above to set up a more extensive orienteering course using a 1:25 000 Ordnance Survey map or a specially-drawn orienteering map at 1:10 000. Check over and carry out a hazard assessment of the whole area prior to the work. In the field, students will find they cannot always follow a straight line between control points and they have to acquire the skill of making observations from the map and the land in order to plot the easiest routes and work out bearings and distances for each leg of the route. For safety reasons students must stay in groups of three and be given a strict time limit for their return. Try to ensure that the start and finish are distinctive landmarks - visible from the whole area - and instruct students to return to either point if they run out of time.

Residential fieldcourses may offer the opportunity to develop these skills further in more open country.

Further sources of help and guidance on preparing orienteering courses include the local orienteering club - find out if there is one in your area and/or look in local bookshops and libraries for orienteering maps and guides or books on orienteering (e.g. McNeill *et al.*, 1998).

Chapter 7

Hydrology on the doorstep

Context

While few schools have access to good river sites within the school locality, key stage 3 students can still explore the hydrological processes which result in stream runoff and therefore control river discharge. Their investigations can focus on precipitation, interception, infiltration and simulated hydrographs from roof runoff. Most hydrological principles concerning how much and how quickly rainfall reaches the river can be established through practical activities, and all the methods described here can be accomplished within the school grounds.

Interception

Aims

- To find out how much rainfall is intercepted by different types of vegetation.
- To consider how interception affects river systems.

Method

Set up a network of school-made raingauges at a variety of sample sites in the open as well as beneath vegetation. The sites beneath vegetation are aimed at collecting rain which has passed through the canopy as *throughfall*. The difference between rainfall in the open and the throughfall represents the amount of rainfall intercepted by the vegetation (and subsequently evaporated back into the atmosphere).

Raingauges can be readily manufactured from large plastic drink bottles. Cut off the top, invert it and insert this 'funnel' into the open body of the bottle. Bury the base of the bottle in the ground or tether it to three pegs pushed into the ground to prevent it from toppling over. On a solid surface the gauge can be held by bricks placed close around it.

Where the amount of rainfall collected has been substantial it is possible to measure the depth of water by simply holding a ruler against the outside of the bottle and taking the measurement in millimetres. This is not a precise equivalent to the actual rainfall amount because the base of drinks bottles are often convex. However, provided all the bottles used are of a standard moulding this does not present a problem. Measure smaller amounts by pouring the rainwater into a measuring cylinder which shows the volume in millilitres. To convert the volume of rainfall in millilitres to the equivalent depth of rainfall in millimetres divide the volume by the cross-sectional area of the bottle.

$$\frac{\text{volume of rainfall in millilitres}}{\text{cross-sectional area of bottle in square millimetres}} = \text{rainfall in millimetres}$$

As the amount of interception varies considerably beneath tree canopies, a number of raingauges need to be set up beneath each vegetation type. Use a minimum of five gauges in each of the following areas:

- in the open (preferably away from buildings),
- beneath bush or shrub vegetation, and
- beneath different tree canopies.

The precise location of the raingauges offers opportunities for a whole-class discussion on the different sampling strategies, e.g. grid or random. Students could look at variations in interception rates beneath different species of tree by comparing those under deciduous with those under coniferous trees.

Results

Calculate a mean rainfall amount for each site. For sites beneath vegetation cover the percentage interception can be calculated as:

$$\text{Interception \% } = \frac{\text{(rainfall in open - rainfall beneath vegetation)}}{\text{rainfall in open}} \times 100$$

Conclusion

In interpreting results students may need to refer to a variety of factors, including:

- density of canopy and type of vegetation
- leaf structure of tree/shrub
- duration and intensity of rainfall
- temperature and evaporation.

The levels of interception associated with tree cover can be linked to the role of forests in the hydrological cycle - particularly in terms of reducing runoff to rivers during storms and returning evaporated water to the atmosphere. This is an excellent topic for making strong connections between findings from the immediate locality and issues of global concern. It also provides a useful reminder of the hydrological reasons for forest conservation as well as the more familiar arguments concerning biodiversity and maintaining the carbon balance of the atmosphere.

Where investigations are carried out at different times of year using the same sites, the role of season can be introduced.

Extension

Students can extend their investigation to include the fact that some rain reaches the ground by stemflow - rain that trickles down plant stems and tree trunks to the ground. Practically-inclined individuals or small groups of students can design and set up stemflow gauges on trees in the school grounds as part of their project/coursework. The tricky part is getting a good seal between the collecting device and the tree trunk without harming the tree.

Infiltration

Aims

- To find out how infiltration rates vary on different surfaces.
- To consider how varying infiltration rates might affect river systems.

Method

Geography departments often measure infiltration rates by producing infiltration rings - essentially a tube inserted into the ground with a ruler held in place inside. Although tin cans with both ends removed are often used they are most likely to buckle when hammered into compacted or stony soil. A more resistant and durable alternative is to cut PVC drainage pipe into 15cm lengths and chamfer one end with a file or sanding disc to produce a sharp, bevelled edge (this eases the insertion of the infiltration ring into the soil). Placing a strong block of wood over the infiltration ring before hammering it into the ground also avoids cracking it. Ensure that the ring is as upright as possible. Good results can only be obtained if the seal between the ring and the surrounding soil is water-tight. If necessary, compress the soil around the outside of it. Water bubbling up around the outside of the ring is a sure sign of a leak.

Students measure the rate of infiltration by placing a ruler in the ring, filling the tube to a specific level (e.g. 100mm) and either recording the new level each minute or timing how long a given depth of water (e.g. 10mm) takes to infiltrate into the soil. They then refill the ring to the initial level and repeat. Reasonable results can be obtained after 10 minutes. To determine the *infiltration capacity* for a site, however, readings will need to be continued until a more or less constant rate of infiltration is reached.

To help students interpret their findings set up a number of experiments, each one focusing on a particular factor affecting the infiltration rate. If many factors are operating simultaneously (e.g. soil and slope angle affecting infiltration) students may find the results difficult to interpret. The following factors can form a basis for sampling.

Soil compaction: Set up infiltration sites along a transect across a footpath or on the games field at intervals away from a goal mouth. Students could establish a grid of sites around a goal mouth which should enable them to draw up an infiltration map with isolines.

Position on slope and slope angle: Set up sites at intervals down a slope and, if possible, survey the slope profile to enable students to plot the sites to be recorded in relation to the gradient.

Hillslope hollows and hillslope spurs: If possible set up sites on different types of slopes to enable students to consider whether hillslope hollows have lower infiltration rates than hillslope spurs. (Hillslope hollows are thought to be important areas in drainage basins for the generation of storm runoff.)

Vegetation: Either locate sites along a transect from grassland into scrub/woodland or set up a random sample of sites in each vegetation type.

Other factors affecting infiltration rates might include soil texture, stoniness, amount of organic matter and moisture content.

Investigation of *temporal* as well as *spatial* variation can be introduced by repeating surveys of the same site in different seasons or before and after rainfall. If possible, obtain discharge data for a nearby river and encourage students to look for seasonal variations in the relationship between rainfall and runoff. They could then relate these to their infiltration data.

Results

Students calculate and compare the mean rate of infiltration for each site. Where the amount of infiltration each minute has been determined then an infiltration rate over time can be plotted. Normally students can fit a reasonable curve to the scatter of points plotted - with infiltration rate declining as soil moisture builds up. If, after some time, the rate of infiltration stabilises students can use this to express the infiltration capacity for that site.

Conclusion

Where students have carried out a number of experiments they can assess the relative importance of a range of factors. Emphasise the significance of infiltration as the key process determining the development of surface runoff, and hence flood risk. For each site students can assess the likelihood of the infiltration rate being exceeded during a rainstorm and surface runoff developing. To make this evaluation, it may be helpful to refer to typical rainfall intensity values. Students will need to calculate the hourly infiltration rate for their sites by multiplying their measurements by an appropriate factor. They can then compare these values with the rainfall intensities shown in Table 1.

Table 1: Typical hourly rainfall intensities in the UK.

Rainfall type	Rainfall intensity (millimetres per hour)
Light drizzle	1–2
Moderate frontal rainfall	3–9
Heavy convectional rainfall	10–20+

Unless the soil is very compacted or the water table is near the surface most sites have infiltration capacities which can cope with all but the most intense rainstorms.

Extension

Students can observe and map where puddles form and the directions in which rainwater flows around the school/fieldwork site during heavy rain.

Roof hydrographs

As part of an introductory discussion students must imagine they are a raindrop falling on the school roof. Ask them to describe the journeys they might experience before ending up as a droplet of water in a cloud.

Aims

- To plot a storm hydrograph of runoff from the school roof.
- To explain the shape of the hydrograph, make comparisons with river hydrographs and apply findings to an understanding of runoff processes in the drainage basin.

Method

Students start by measuring rainfall and runoff amounts at the onset of significant rainfall and continue with recording until flow stops. This activity is difficult to fit into the timetable as it is entirely rainfall dependent! Students will need to be briefed in advance and mobilised at short notice. The activity is well suited to individual or small group project work during a rainy lunch hour or could be undertaken by some students at home. All that is needed is access to a downpipe draining rainwater from a roof gutter, a bucket and a school-made raingauge (see page 41).

Ensure that the bottom of the downpipe has sufficient clearance to allow runoff to be collected in a small bucket or large measuring cylinder. Students measure runoff at frequent, regular, intervals (every 5 or 10 minutes) by placing a receptacle of known volume under the downpipe and recording the time it takes to fill in seconds. They then calculate the runoff in litres per second.

Opportunities for useful interpretations are much increased if students can also measure rainfall totals for each 5 or 10 minute period. Where rainfall is light they should use a large diameter funnel and a narrow measuring cylinder to collect the rainwater. To determine rainfall amounts in millimetres, divide the volume of water collected in millilitres by the area of the funnel in square millimetres.

$$\frac{\text{volume in millilitres}}{\text{area of funnel in square millimetres}} = \text{rainfall amount in millimetres}$$

Results

- Plot the rainfall as bar charts and runoff as a line graph with a common timescale.
- Measure the lag time from the time of highest rainfall intensity to the time of peak runoff and annotate the hydrograph components.

Conclusion

Students should be able to draw some of the following conclusions from a roof runoff hydrograph and these can be related to rivers and drainage basins.

1 As with river hydrographs, the rising limb on the graph is normally steeper than the recession - the flow after the rainfall being sustained by pooled water (= storage) in the gutter. This is analogous to storage in a drainage basin but on roofs the absence of soil or groundwater storage results in a more rapid recession.

2 Runoff is zero prior to rainfall and a little while after it stops - an obvious point, but one which reinforces the importance of water storage in river basins in sustaining flow when it does not rain.

3 Roof runoff produces very short lag times - a function of all the flow occurring over the surface and the very short distance from roof top (= watershed) to downpipe (= river mouth) compared to a real river basin.

4 More prolonged, steady rainfall may produce a virtually flat-topped hydrograph, a feature not normally found on river hydrographs. Again differences in storage characteristics can be discussed, the roof having limited storage so that after a certain time has elapsed input = output.

5 Have a whole class discussion on the similarities between runoff from a roof and runoff from urban catchments.

Extension

Build up a set of hydrographs for rainstorms of different intensities and durations and at different seasons. This will enable you to discuss most of the ideas concerning changes in river flow over time with your students.

Mathematically-inclined students can calculate the total amount of rain falling on a roof compared to the amount of runoff. The percentage of rainfall running off is usually very high, though will vary according to the season and evaporation loss. These calculations often give surprisingly high volumes of water, a finding that could be linked with water conservation issues and the possibility of storing water for irrigating school gardens and playing fields.

Chapter 8

Weather and climate

There is a long tradition in geography teaching of operating a manual school weather station to collect weather data on a regular basis. In some cases long runs of weather data were gathered, while in others the station was used intermittently, i.e. when a class was covering weather topics. The manual weather station served to demonstrate basic meteorological instrumentation as well as allowing weather changes to be monitored and related to published weather charts. Now many such weather stations have either been dismantled or have fallen into disuse. In some cases the school has replaced the manual weather station with an automatic one. A number of important advantages and disadvantages of using manual and automatic weather recording are shown in Figure 7.

Figure 7 indicates that the two systems have quite distinct educational purposes. While manual stations are likely to have limitations in terms of continuity of data, using them to record and observe weather will contribute to students' conceptual understanding and their sensory experience of the changing weather. The concept of relative humidity, for example, becomes clearer once students have used a wet and dry bulb thermometer. Likewise, using the Beaufort scale is a valuable reminder that the human senses can be as valid as mechanical or

Figure 7: Some of the advantages and disadvantages of automatic and manually operated weather stations.

Type of weather station	Advantages	Disadvantages
Manually operated weather station with: Stevenson screen, maximum, minimum, wet and dry bulb thermometers, raingauge and wind vane. Windspeed recorded on the Beaufort scale, atmospheric pressure from an indoor barograph, aneroid or mercury barometer	• Using the instruments assists the understanding of meteorological concepts and processes • Students personally involved in observations and recording, and 'sense' the weather as well as recording it • Faulty equipment is easily diagnosed	• Some instruments vulnerable to accidental damage and vandalism • Some instruments expensive to replace • Difficult to maintain continuity of readings over weekends and holidays
Automatic weather station with: continuous recording of temperature, relative humidity, windspeed, direction, sunshine hours, atmospheric pressure and hourly rainfall	• Continuous recording even when school is closed • Instant display and comparison of weather variables on computer screen • Often a greater range of weather variables can be recorded • Mast can be located out of reach of interference	• The instrumentation itself has limited contribution to the learning process in terms of conceptual understanding • Faulty equipment difficult to diagnose and replace • Can diminish the opportunity for sensory experience of weather

electronic devices in observing and recording. The continuity of data collected by an automatic station will enable a fuller picture of temporal change to emerge, as well as allowing easier exploration of the relationships and connections between weather variables. However, the act of sitting in front of a computer screen downloading data from a mast on the school roof tends to reinforce the perception of the geographer as a detached observer of the world rather than as a participant immersed in her or his surroundings.

Combining primary weather data with secondary sources

Aims

- To observe and record changes in local weather over time.
- To relate local changes to atmospheric processes and the regional atmospheric circulation.

Method

Using either manual or automatic weather stations, students collect basic weather data over a week or more. In the case of manual data, readings taken at convenient standardised times each day should be adequate. Data from automatic stations can be downloaded hourly and plotted, allowing students to explore diurnal as well as day-to-day variations.

Obtain daily records from secondary data sources in order to set the local weather changes in their regional context and develop explanations of changing weather patterns. These secondary sources can include MetFAX, shipping forecasts recorded from radio broadcasts or weather data from websites.

MetFAX data

This Met Office service can be used to access a range of meteorological information including:

- Daily weather charts for the UK and North Atlantic showing isobars, fronts, pressure systems and weather reports for selected sites.
- Infra-red satellite images for the same areas.

To receive MetFAX information, set fax machine to 'poll receive' mode and dial **09003 400480** for a list of services, e.g. numbers to dial for the synoptic chart, the satellite image, regional forecasts. It is as well to check the costs and duration of each service as the transmissions are charged at premium rates. *Weather Packs* are also available via MetFAX; these include satellite images and weather charts for either the UK or the North Atlantic.

In case of difficulties there is a MetFAX helpline, telephone: 08700 750075.

Shipping forecasts

More able students can use atmospheric pressure and wind direction data from the shipping forecast broadcasts on Radio 4 to plot their own UK weather maps. Provide a base map showing the locations of the coastal weather reporting stations and record the broadcast to enable the report to be paused during the plotting process.

Where students have the ability to interpolate and a knowledge and understanding of wind directions within low and high pressure systems they could attempt to plot isobars on a map of the UK.

Met Office website

This website (www.met-office.gov.uk) allows access to infra-red and visible spectrum satellite images for the UK and North Atlantic. These are updated daily on website: www.met-office.gov.uk/satpics. The cloud patterns on the infra-red image are useful for picking out weather systems, especially if used in conjunction with the synoptic chart.

This website also contains daily weather data which covers recent months. The data is collected from 15 manually-operated weather stations evenly distributed across the UK. It can be downloaded to allow students to make comparisons and look for temporal changes. Weather charts for comparison with satellite images and a host of other international links can be downloaded from website: www.met.rdg.ac.uk/~brugge/bi.html

Results

Students can enter either manually- or automatically-derived weather data into a spreadsheet and graph or chart the results to summarise the changes in weather variables over time. Spreadsheet software now enables students to superimpose line graphs onto bar charts and include two different 'y' axes on either side of the graph. This helps them to see relationships between weather variables, e.g. rainfall in millimetres against atmospheric pressure (mb). By plotting weather variables and atmospheric pressure over time, students will be able to see relationships in the data and can move towards an understanding of atmospheric processes.

Interpretation

One possible framework to help students interpret changes in weather over time is to ask them to answer a range of questions. For example:

- What changes do you notice in the weather when pressure rises/falls?
- On the synoptic charts and satellite images can you pick out any fronts, and, if so, did they pass your weather site during the study?
- What changes occurred in the weather as the fronts passed?

- From the synoptic charts were there any periods of high pressure?

- What was distinctive about the weather at these times?

- What have you found out from this study that could help you forecast weather using a weather chart and satellite image?

Extension

To apply students' understanding of the connections between weather maps and satellite images on the one hand and weather on the ground on the other, give them copies of the current synoptic chart and satellite image of the UK and ask them to compile a forecast. Student-produced weather forecasts can then be compared to those from radio, television, MetFAX or the Internet and both of these compared to actual observations of weather on the ground. As the ability of students to forecast the weather improves, display their results on the geography noticeboard. (Their peers will be quick to point out any inaccuracies!)

Weather and air pollution

Air quality data is not readily obtained from primary sources. While some schools have a carbon monoxide meter (useful for carrying out roadside air quality surveys) among the science or health education resources, such equipment is beyond the budget of most geography departments. An alternative approach is for students to gather air quality data from secondary sources and compare it with their primary weather data.

Aims

- To investigate variation in air quality over time using secondary data.
- To investigate variation in weather variables over the same time period using primary data collection methods.
- To investigate the relationship between air quality and weather.

Method

Secondary air quality data

Secondary data for air quality for both urban and rural sites is available from the Department of Environment, Transport and the Regions (DETR) Air Pollution Information Service. This data is continually updated and can be accessed in the following ways:

- via the DETR website: www.environment.detr.gov.uk/airq/aqinfo.htm,
- by telephoning the freephone number: 0800 556677, and/or
- by monitoring Ceefax (page 41017) or Teletext (page 106) on television.

The website lists air quality variables, these include: Nitrogen dioxide, Sulphur dioxide, Carbon monoxide, Ozone, Particulates (PM10s), and two types of Hydrocarbons (Benzene and 1,3 Butadiene).

The number and spread of sites monitored should enable you or your students to identify a location reasonably close to the school and log or download the appropriate data. There are currently over 50 monitoring sites listed, mainly in urban areas, with several sites in each major city. The data is updated every three hours so students can monitor changes over quite short time spans and compare them to local first-hand weather data. The DETR website is a particularly useful resource for both current and past air quality data. It combines detailed archives of data from the monitoring network with data gathered at monitoring stations operated by local authorities and research institutions. All of this information can be downloaded to school computer systems.

Figure 8 shows characteristic values for Nitrogen dioxide and Sulphur dioxide obtained from the DETR Air Pollution Information Service. Data are quoted for a range of UK sites for two dates with contrasting weather conditions: the first

Figure 8: Air pollution data from secondary sources in parts per billion (ppb).

Nitrogen dioxide concentrations (ppb)		
Town/area	10/6/93	9/7/93
Edinburgh	51	30
Glasgow	65	8
Belfast	73	27
Teesside	28	22
Leeds	62	27
Manchester	67	24
West Midlands	32	30
Birmingham	76	17
London Bloomsbury	122	41
London Victoria	109	35
London kerbside	138	42
London Earls Court	120	30
Cardiff	30	26
Merseyside	90	26
Bristol	65	23
Newcastle upon Tyne	62	39
Derbyshire	29	7
South East England	11	1
Hertfordshire	31	5
Northern Scotland	3	0

Sulphur dioxide concentrations (ppb)		
Town/area	10/6/93	9/7/93
Edinburgh	7	9
Sunderland	4	3
Belfast	109	13
Birmingham	19	7
Leeds	27	32
South Yorkshire	62	5
Hertfordshire	12	15
London Bloomsbury	41	9
London Victoria	53	8
London kerbside	36	15
Cardiff	16	3
Merseyside	78	4
Newcastle upon Tyne	8	8
Bristol	14	16
Northern Scotland	4	0
Derbyshire	25	12
South East England	7	4

column (10 June 1993) under anticyclonic conditions with low wind speeds and the second column (9 July 1993) under the influence of a stronger westerly airstream.

Primary weather data

Daily recordings of atmospheric pressure, windspeed and possibly wind direction (see pages 50 and 55-56) may be useful in interpreting variations in air quality.

Either you or your students will need to collect data from both sources for air quality and weather variables over a number of days. Ideally this timescale should include periods of high pressure and stable air as well as low pressure with frontal systems.

Results

Students can produce combination graphs showing atmospheric pressure, windspeed and the concentration of each pollutant. This should indicate any relationships in the data. Students can then compile scattergraphs for each pollutant against:

1 atmospheric pressure, and

2 windspeed.

Older or more able students could attempt to test for correlations between the primary and secondary data.

Interpretation

Discuss the relationships between the concentration of pollutants and atmospheric conditions in terms of atmospheric processes - one particular example is the role of 'dispersal' in affecting air quality.

Where students are analysing ozone data they will find the spatial patterns are often rather different from other pollutants. This is because ozone is a secondary pollutant formed from the interaction of other gases. Interestingly, the highest concentrations of ozone may well be found at rural sites.

Students will also need to consider the sources of pollutants. The most important are the relative contributions and different compositions of traffic and industrial

Figure 9: Typical concentrations and simplified recommended limits for air pollutants in parts per million (ppm)/parts per billion (ppb). Note: * limit values vary according to period of exposure.

Pollutant	Normal concentration in unpolluted air	Typical concentration in polluted air	Recommended EU limit*
Carbon monoxide	0.01–0.02 ppm	1–100 ppm	10 ppm
Nitrogen dioxide	0.1–0.5 ppb	20–300 ppb	105 ppb
Sulphur dioxide	1–2 ppb	5–400 ppb	100 ppb

emissions. The DETR website includes useful information on sources of pollutants. Students can use this to compare the concentration of specific pollutants with the recommended European Union limits. Figure 9 presents typical concentrations in polluted and unpolluted air and simplified limit values for specific pollutants.

Extension

Students can use the information provided on the DETR website to explore the variations in pollutants in different parts of the UK. They could compile pollution maps from the downloaded data and use these to examine the variations across the country under different weather systems. This activity can be extended to comparing satellite images (downloaded from the Met Office website) with the students' pollution maps.

If your school has long-term weather data on file, students could compare this with similar air pollution data from the website archive.

Where the DETR website shows an air quality monitoring site in a roadside location close to the school, download the data for this site. Ask students to carry out traffic surveys close to this site and compare their results with the downloaded data.

There is also the possibility of comparing secondary air quality data with the health of local people, e.g. asthma sufferers. While it is important to avoid stigmatising students suffering from asthma, volunteers could keep a diary of their health, to include details of how often they had to use their inhaler, which can then be compared to the air quality record.

Microclimates in the school grounds

A common problem with the organisation of microclimate studies is the availability of replicate sets of equipment which enable the whole class to be fully involved. This activity focuses on a cheap and simple method for recording windspeed and direction so that large numbers of sites can be surveyed, and enables all students to be occupied in gathering and mapping the information.

Aims

- To record and map variations in windspeed and direction in the school grounds.
- To apply the results in decision making contexts.

Method

Students will need a large-scale base map of the school grounds for locating and plotting the recording sites. Introduce them to the merits of different sampling strategies and organise them into groups of two or three.

Choose a number of different sites and instruct students to release a styrofoam (polystyrene) packing chip of standard shape and size from a height of 2m above ground level at each sample point. They must note the point where the chip first touches the ground and record (in metres) the distance travelled and the direction (either as a true bearing or an estimate based on the eight points of the compass). Variations caused by gusts of wind can be accommodated to some extent by calculating the mean of three readings at each site. Problems may arise close to buildings where eddying and vortices may cause the chip to be blown upwards. Tell students that this in itself is worth recording.

While some chips may go astray in high winds, remind students of the importance of avoiding litter. Styrofoam is notoriously non-degradable. (You also need to hang on to those chips because styrofoam may soon be banned as packaging material!) Using potato crisps or puffy types of food snack is more environmentally friendly, but reports have been received of students eating their equipment before the fieldwork is complete!

Results

Groups of students plot the mean distance travelled onto a base map together with an arrow to show wind direction. Each group then shares their data with the whole class. Where reasonably straightforward patterns emerge, students can attempt to join points of equal windspeed to create isolines.

Interpretation

Introduce the role of buildings and trees in creating shelter, funnelling and eddying, and identify and explain sites of highest and lowest windspeed. Identify a number of possible scenarios to which students could apply their findings, for example:

- locating an optimum site for a wind turbine (see Chapter 9, pages 59-65),
- where to plant trees to create a more sheltered environment, and
- locating areas for seating, recreational use or a school garden.

Extension

If sufficient equipment is available you could incorporate temperature recording into the microclimate studies. Reasonably low cost digital thermometers are excellent alternatives to fragile glass ones. These digital thermometers (which often incorporate a humidity sensor) enable students to take readings on the ground as well as at a specified height above it. To ensure comparability between sites it is helpful to specify a time period (e.g. two minutes) for the sensors to stabilise, and to ensure that the instrument is shaded from direct sun. The combination of temperature, humidity and windspeed data should enable students to establish correlations between microclimate variables.

The students can compare their first-hand data on windspeeds and direction and diaries on the health of hay-fever sufferers in the same way that air quality data can be compared with the health of local people. Students can look for correlations between the diaries, their own windspeed and direction data and information on pollen counts from the BBC website (www.bbc.co.uk/weather/features/pollen.shtml).

Chapter 9

Energy studies

These activities are based around the school buildings and grounds and integrate aspects of the geography curriculum with science and Information Technology, and the cross-curricular theme of environmental education.

A scheme of fieldwork based around the theme of renewable energy and microclimates is presented in Figure 10. Start the investigation with a consideration of the range of both conventional and renewable energy resources and their associated environmental impacts. Follow this with a discussion of the main sources of energy used in the UK and what environmental impacts are thought to be involved in the generating processes. Then focus on the types of energy used in the school and by students in their homes. The intention here is to develop the students' thinking about the amount of energy consumed by the school infrastructure, to consider possible areas for energy conservation, and to undertake practical activities which determine how much energy could be generated from renewable sources within the school premises.

Energy audits

Aims

- To find out the amount of electrical energy consumed on the school premises.
- To find out how much energy is consumed by different activities.
- To consider where and how energy could be conserved.

Method

Obtain readings from the school meter(s) over a set time period and calculate the total units (kilowatt hours) of electricity used on the school premises for a day and/or a week. The students then need to discover how much electricity is used during different activities by auditing the energy consumption of the school.

The audit method is ideally suited to work with spreadsheets (Figure 11 shows a worked example of such an audit). The process of data collection requires careful organisation because students will need to access as much of the school building as possible without causing disturbance. Small groups of students can be allocated a number of rooms to survey and asked to carry out the activity during break times. Students should:

Level and curriculum/ syllabus links	Key question/Aim	Introductory activities	Fieldwork objectives	Fieldwork activity	Equipment	Follow-up	Extensions	Action
Key stage 3	How much electrical energy is used on the school premises i) in a day? ii) in a year?	Review of conventional energy production. Review what energy sources are used on the school premises and for what (electricity, oil, gas, coal). Sensory activity outdoors – what forms of natural energy can you feel/see/hear?	Find out how much electrical energy is used on the school premises.	Carry out an energy audit using a spreadsheet (Figure 11 shows an example). To check results with actual use obtain meter readings from caretaker and electricity bill information from bursar.	PC with *Excel* spreadsheet (or equivalent). Printout of blank spreadsheet for field recording.	Enter energy audit data into spreadsheet to determine daily use. Chart use for lighting, heating, cooking, electronic equipment separately. To compute annual use separate term time and holiday estimates will be needed.	Discuss and review the energy uses of different appliances. Where could energy savings be made?	Compile an energy conservation policy in consultation with school management, bursar, caretaker, etc. Present policy to the whole school, implement and monitor.
GCSE/ Key stage 4	How much energy could be generated by wind turbines on the school premises?	Discuss some of the advantages and disadvantages of wind energy compared to other renewables.	How much energy could be generated from wind in the school grounds? What would be the best location for a wind turbine?	Carry out anemometer survey at sample sites within the school grounds. Repeat under different weather conditions to give mean values for each site.	Base map of school grounds. Hand held anemometers (DIY versions can be used if calibrated carefully). Specification data for a medium sized wind turbine.	Compute mean windspeeds in metres per second. Use power graph for a specific turbine to predict power output at each site at the mean windspeed recorded (see Figure 12 for a 6.5kW turbine).	Estimate annual energy output from windspeed data (figure). Refer to annual energy use figures from audit. Determine the number of turbines needed to supply the school.	If results look promising set up a feasibility study to determine costings and sources of funding for a wind energy project.

Figure 10: A field-based scheme of work for investigating renewable energy and microclimates.

1 Identify and record all electrical appliances in each room in the school.

2 Find out the power rating of each appliance in kilowatts (kW).

3 Estimate the number of hours in 24 that the appliance is in use.

Appliance	Power rating in watts (W)	A Power rating in kilowatts (kW) (W/1000)	B Number of appliances	C Average hours of use per day (if less than 1 hr enter as decimal of hr)	D Daily power consumption kWh A x B x C	Cost per day £ Dx0.0773
Lighting: low energy light bulb	10	0.010	3	6.00	0.18	0.01
Lighting: striplight	20	0.020	4	6.00	0.48	0.04
Lighting: 40W bulb	40	0.040	4	6.00	0.96	0.07
Lighting: 60W bulb	60	0.060	6	6.00	2.16	0.17
Lighting: 100W bulb	100	0.100	3	6.00	1.80	0.14
Photocopier (in use)	1350	1.350	0	1.00	0.00	0.00
Photocopier (on standby)	100	0.100	0	8.00	0.00	0.00
Computer and monitor	45	0.045	2	6.00	0.54	0.04
Computer printer	50	0.050	1	6.00	0.30	0.02
Fridge	60	0.060	1	24.00	1.44	0.11
Freezer	60	0.060	1	24.00	1.44	0.11
Television	115	0.115	1	4.00	0.46	0.04
Stereo	130	0.130	1	2.00	0.26	0.02
Washing machine	1300	1.300	1	1.00	1.30	0.10
Hairdrier	2000	2.000	1	0.10	0.20	0.02
Iron	1300	1.300	1	0.50	0.65	0.05
Dishwasher	1600	1.600	1	1.00	1.60	0.12
Toaster	1750	1.750	1	0.20	0.35	0.03
Electric cooker (per ring)	2000	2.000	4	0.20	1.60	0.12
Electric cooker (grill)	2000	2.000	1	0.20	0.40	0.03
Electric cooker (oven)	3000	3.000	1	1.50	4.50	0.35
Convector heater	2000	2.000	1	3.00	6.00	0.46
Kettle	2200	2.200	1	0.50	1.10	0.09
Water boiler	3000	3.000	0	0.00	0.00	0.00
Immersion heater	3000	3.000	1	3.00	9.00	0.70
Fan heater	3000	3.000	1	2.00	6.00	0.46
Fax (standby)	120	0.120	0	0.00	0.00	0.00
Storage heater	2000	2.000	2	8.00	32.00	2.47
Totals					74.72	5.78

Figure 11: An energy audit spreadsheet

Power ratings are normally displayed in watts or kilowatts along with other specifications on the back or underside of electrical equipment. You can build estimates into the spreadsheets to avoid students having to touch electrical equipment unnecessarily. (Some average ratings are included in Figure 11.) Equipment such as photocopiers and computer printers can be problematic in that they have two power modes:

1 'standby', which has a low power consumption, and

2 'operation' which has a higher power consumption than 'standby' above.

These machines may be on 'standby' for much of the time and in 'operation' for brief periods only. Incorporate separate entries in the spreadsheet for standby and operational modes, each with a separate power rating and the hours of usage.

Results

Calculations for the power usage of each category of equipment can be calculated in the spreadsheet by multiplying together the cells containing:

- number of items of each type of equipment,
- average power rating, and
- average hours of use in 24.

This gives a power consumption figure for each type of appliance in kilowatt hours (kWh). One killowatt hour equals one 'unit' of electricity on electricity meters and bills.

Students can compile summary tables and charts showing power consumption for different parts of the school (e.g. classrooms, laboratories, offices, catering areas, sports facilities) or different functions (e.g. heating, ventilation, cooking, lighting, ICT use). Their results can be checked against actual electricity usage from meter readings and electricity bills.

Note: This method covers electrical energy consumption only. Many schools have oil or gas powered hot water and central heating systems which require separate energy consumption calculations. Students can convert the amount of fuel used in these systems to kilowatt hours to produce a more complete energy audit.

Conclusion

A whole-class discussion centring on which activities consume the most power will normally indicate heavier consumption by heating or cooking appliances compared to the lower consumption of electronic equipment such as computers and peripherals. While lighting has a relatively low consumption per light bulb, the large numbers in use (particularly during the winter months) may make lighting the highest overall electricity user.

This approach offers ample scope for students to consider their personal actions in relation to energy conservation both in school and at home. The size of the daily electricity bill for the school buildings may be quite startling.

Extension

This activity can be extended to an investigation of the cost and power savings of installing low-energy lights and/or making periodic surveys of lights left on in unoccupied rooms. Another possible activity is the implementation of energy conservation. This is more likely to be successful where students influence their peers. Having identified areas where savings can be made, groups of students, in consultation with the school management team, could organise an energy conservation campaign throughout the school.

Students could negotiate with management to ensure that any savings made as a result of their endeavours are channelled into further conservation projects rather than the money saved being 'swallowed up' by the school budget. These might include the wind turbine project outlined below or other conservation efforts such as the establishment or improvement of a school recycling scheme.

A wind energy feasibility study

Aims

- To measure wind velocities around the school to determine the optimum siting for a wind turbine.
- To use wind recordings to predict the power output from a wind turbine.
- To compare the predicted output from wind energy with the energy requirements of the school from the energy audit.

Method

Students carry out a survey of local windspeeds. This can be based on the methods described on pages 55-56, but if the styrofoam chip method is used then the distances travelled by the chips will need to be converted to metres per second by also measuring the time in seconds it takes each one to travel a given distance. Alternatively, if available, hand held anemometers can be used at a height of 2m above ground level.

Either method gives windspeed values near ground level. Figure 12 shows a power output graph for a 6.5kW wind turbine mounted 12m above ground level. Student-measured windspeeds at 2m can be converted by using a figure of x1.5 to predict the windspeed at 12m, although the conversion factor varies greatly depending on surface roughness and turbulence.

Results

The wind survey enables students to locate the optimum site for a wind turbine in the school grounds, and they can estimate the predicted power output using Figure 12. To obtain more reliable estimates of power output ask students to repeat their windspeed surveys under different weather conditions this will help them determine a mean windspeed for the site over a given period of time.

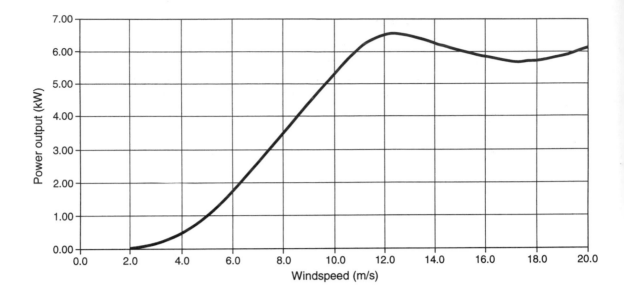

Figure 12: Power output for a 6.5kW, 12m high wind turbine.

Figure 13: Predicted annual energy output for a range of mean annual windspeeds.

More reliable estimates of windpower really require a mean annual windspeed to be determined. This may be possible if an automatic weather station is in operation. Ensure that the windspeed values are converted to metres per second before the students use the graphs in Figures 12 and 13. If an approximate mean annual windspeed is available for the school site students can use Figure 13 to predict an annual power output, and compare this to the annual electricity consumption for the school. One wind turbine may well be insufficient for a large school, but smaller schools in exposed sites may end up with surplus energy!

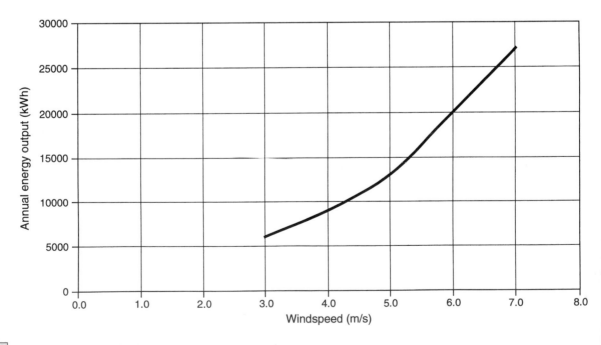

Conclusion

The practical feasibility of installing a wind turbine obviously involves a range of other factors, not least the cost of installation compared to the value of electricity generated. The installation costs quoted for the 6.5kW turbine (to which Figures 12 and 13 relate) are around £10 000. Ask your students to discover:

- How this cost compares to the value of the electricity produced.
- How many years of electricity generation need to elapse before the turbine will have paid for its installation.

Extension

Students can transfer the knowledge and understanding they have acquired through local fieldwork on energy studies into changes towards a more sustainable school infrastructure. A student-based initiative might begin by publicising the feasibility study in a local newspaper and seeking sources of funding from local businesses to take the project further (e.g. the extensions of the energy audit pages 59-63). A few schools already operate wind turbines very successfully.

Solar power installations on school roofs are an increasingly common sight and a similar project aimed at assessing the potential of solar power offers students the opportunity to undertake local fieldwork by adapting the approach described above. This can be based on the geography national curriculum and has cross-curricular implications.

Traffic surveys and sustainable transport

Context

Traffic surveys recur frequently in local fieldwork because such data can usually be gathered in close proximity to the school site. The process of data collection develops students' skills in observation, recording, organisation and co-operation. In addition, processing the information obtained develops useful skills in tabulation, computing percentages and graphing or charting results, either manually or using spreadsheets.

While the activity is justified in terms of skills development, the geographical content is often limited. It may not go beyond the comparison of different streets or analysis of variations in traffic flow at different times of day. However, traffic surveys can be set in contexts which encourage students' thinking about the fundamental choices concerning transport policy.

Aims

- To determine how much fuel is being burned over a time period in local streets.
- To determine the quantity of CO_2 (carbon dioxide) emissions from traffic over a time period in local streets.

Method

Students carry out straightforward calculations for the fuel use and CO_2 emissions from a traffic survey using the data on fuel use per kilometre and CO_2 emissions per kilometre shown in Figure 14. In the field students record vehicle counts per hour and classify the data collected into the categories in Figure 14. They should also record approximate average speed of travel. This can be done by timing vehicles over a measured length of street, calculating their speeds and working out an average (15km per hour is typical for fairly heavy urban traffic).

Mode of transport	Fuel consumption (l/km*)	CO_2 emission per km (kg)
Cyclist	0.002	0.005
Pedestrian	0.007	0.018
Motorcycle	0.079	0.200
Car	0.095	0.240
Taxi	0.100	0.253
Van/minibus	0.120	0.304
Small HGV	0.250	0.633
Bus	0.400	1.012
Double decker bus	0.420	1.063
Large HGV	0.550	1.392

Figure 14: Fuel consumption and CO_2 emission per kilometre for different forms of transport. Note: * for human powered transport the fuel equivalent of the food energy required is quoted.

Results

The students compile or use a spreadsheet which lists:

1 Categories of traffic.

2 Number of vehicles per hour.

3 Average vehicle speed.

4 The fuel consumption figures from Figure 14.

A worked example for a street in Camden, North London, is shown in Figure 15.

Mode of transport	Number per hour	Estimated fuel consumed (l/km*)	CO_2 (kg/km)	Average speed (kph)	Fuel use (litres)	CO_2 total (kg)
Cycles	23	0.002	0.005	12	0.6	1.4
Cars	1508	0.095	0.240	10	1432.6	3619.2
Buses	62	0.400	1.012	7	173.6	439.2
HGV (lge)	88	0.550	1.392	8	387.2	980.0
Vans/minibuses	358	0.250	0.633	10	895.0	2266.1
Taxis	42	0.100	0.253	11	46.2	116.9
M/cycle	48	0.079	0.200	20	75.8	192.0
Total	2129				3011.0	7614.8

Figure 15: Traffic counts collected by students from Acland Burleigh School for the main road outside the school in Camden, North London with estimated fuel use and CO_2 emissions over one hour. Note: * for human powered transport the fuel equivalent of the food energy required is quoted.

Type of transport	Fuel consumption (l/person/km*)	CO_2 emissions (kg/person/km)
Car (driver only)	0.095	0.24
Motorcycle	0.079	0.20
Car (4 passengers)	0.024	0.06
Bus (25 passengers)	0.016	0.05
Underground	0.023	0.05
Pedestrian	0.007	negligible
Bus (70 passengers)	0.006	0.02
Suburban train (250 passengers)	0.005	0.01
Cyclist	0.002	negligible

Figure 16: Fuel use and CO_2 emissions per person per kilometre for different types of passenger transport. Note: * for human powered transport the fuel equivalent of the food energy required is quoted.

Interpretation

The figures in the spreadsheet will provide tangible evidence at the local level of the large amounts of fossil fuel and carbon emissions associated with urban transport systems. This should allow a link between what is happening on the students' doorstep and at global level to be made. One possible approach is to get students to work out the fuel use and carbon emissions for journeys to school. They should take account of different means of transport and the distance travelled. The necessary conversion figures are given in Figure 16. Each student (and teacher!) calculates their share of fuel consumption and carbon emission involved in the daily journey to and from school. The results of this mini survey often lead into discussion of what other factors (e.g. cost, safety, time, fitness) affect our transport decisions and why we do not always choose the most environmentally-compatible method.

Conclusion

Though based on simple field methods, this investigation encourages students to think about the dilemma between the high levels of mobility to which we have become accustomed and the impacts of road transport on resource consumption, climate change and health.

Extension

The whole class could consider what changes in transport policy would be needed (particularly in relation to relative costs and safety) in order to encourage a shift towards less harmful modes of urban transport. Sustrans and RAC can supply information which will help in this context (see page 80).

Chapter 11

Food mile surveys

Context

'Food mile' surveys (so-called even though students measure in kilometres) are simply a measure of the distance which food is transported from its place of production to the retail outlet (e.g. supermarket, greengrocers, street market) or our plates.

Aims

- To establish the places of origin of the food we eat and the 'Food miles' associated with its transportation.
- To raise awareness of the ecological, economic and social issues concerning where food is produced and consumed.

Method

Students collect the necessary information simply by making a trip to the high street, superstore or the school canteen and compiling an inventory of selected food items and their place of origin. As processed foods contain a number of ingredients they are more complex to analyse using this method. Fruit and vegetables are the easiest foods to collect data for because the country of origin is usually marked on the supermarket shelf or the item itself.

Results

On returning to the classroom, students use maps and atlases to locate the sources of each food item, measure the distances they travel, plot the details on a map and tabulate the data. In order to draw out generalities and focus on particular economic, ecological and ethical issues, some sort of classification of raw data may be helpful. This could be based on the following five categories:

1 local UK produced (<50km)

2 other UK produced (>50km)

3 imported food which could have been home produced

4 imported food which can be seasonally grown in UK

5 imported food which cannot be grown in UK

Alternative classifications according to distance-defined zones or continents are possible. Key questions can provide contexts for a food miles surveys, for example:

- To what extent is our food supply related to UK production, the European Union or the global economy?
- If a large proportion of food is coming from distant places what is the effect on energy consumption, traffic and pollution?
- Of the food coming from distant places which items could be easily produced closer to home?, which are seasonally available in the UK?, and which can only be grown in different climates?
- What are the effects on poorer countries of growing high value cash crops for export to distant richer countries?
- Are there differences in the 'food miles' for particular items depending on where they are bought (e.g. different supermarkets, high street greengrocer, street market, farmers' market)?

Conclusion

'Food mile' surveys offer plenty of scope for differentiation because the interpretations and issues raised vary from straightforward to economically and ethically complex. Using a common set of data, students of all abilities can produce a number of pieces of individual work on 'Food miles'. 'Food miles' work can also be used to encourage students to follow through the findings of their investigation into personal decisions. For example, are they prepared to go without the mange-tout from Zimbabwe or the baby sweetcorn from Thailand if it would contribute to a fairer and more sustainable world?

Extension

'Food miles' provide a useful focus for discussions about sustainable development at key stage 4 and beyond because it encourages older students to think about the economic effects of international trade as well as the ecological impacts of a global economy. However, this activity should be handled carefully to counter over-simplistic interpretations. For example, ethnic foodstores or market stalls may import most of their produce because foods associated with particular cultures often cannot be grown in the UK. In this context the role of specific foods in helping sustaining cultures away from their places of origin may be more important than any ecological arguments.

Some teachers argue that students may interpret their 'food mile' findings as being 'anti-international trade' or 'promoting a return to diets based only on local and seasonal foods'. This is not the intention of such studies. Their purpose is rather to encourage student questioning of some recent developments in trade and food retailing. Nowadays products such as milk, potatoes, onions and meat are often transported long distances when they could be sourced locally (with large savings in energy use and carbon emissions). The apocryphal tales of huge trucks roaring across Europe carrying identical commodities but travelling in opposite directions can form a useful focus for discussion.

Careful consideration should also be given to the importance of the long-established trading links whereby tropical crops have been made available to temperate regions and how such trade contributes to the economy of the exporting country while adding variety to western diets.

There is scope for developing critical thinking around the practice of importing seasonally-available temperate crops (e.g. strawberries, raspberries, tomatoes, new potatoes) from distant countries, often by air freight, in order to maintain year-round availability in the UK. Students will discover that this has resulted in a shift away from eating certain foods only when they are 'in season'. This has been identified as one of the ways in which the global economy has severed our connections with the natural world and the cycle of the seasons.

All of the above issues are rich ground for whole-class discussion, with abundant opportunity for values education and debate concerning the role of supermarkets and transnational corporations in influencing and controlling western eating habits.

Chapter 12

Multicultural biogeography

Context

'It seems to me a paradox that whilst we more or less accept that Britain is a multicultural society, our attitudes to foreigners, especially innocent green ones, is in need of some overhauling' (Agyeman, 1998, p. 28).

This is how Julian Agyeman begins a critique of much of what has been taught in biogeography and ecology about 'alien' and 'native' plant species. It highlights how some of the terminology and ideas from ecology teaching may conflict with multicultural teaching. A familiar ecological argument often put forward to favour 'native' over 'alien' species is based on research which identified 284 invertebrate species associated with the 'native' English oak and 43 on the introduced sycamore. Researchers postulated that native tree species lead to greater biodiversity in general and that ecosystems based on introduced species would be less diverse. Later research showed that other native trees supported insect species similar in number to those found on sycamore, and that what matters is the biomass of invertebrate fauna rather than the species diversity. Agyeman (1998) expands on this theme by showing that there is a highly diverse semi-wild flora in cities which has developed over a long period of time. Agyeman found that this flora includes a mix of native species, and both historical and recent introductions (Agyeman, 1998).

This activity, though firmly rooted(!) in geographical methods and concepts, integrates geography, science, history and multicultural education. Students need access to Julian Agyeman's *People, Places and Plants* (1995) and Richard Mabey's *Flora Brittanica* (1996). These two books provide evidence on the geographical origins of plants and set plants in a cultural context - which includes the significance of them in children's folklore.

Aims

- To develop an understanding of the origins of the local flora.
- To develop an appreciation of and respect for the diversity of plant life in the locality.
- To appreciate the significance of wild plants in culture.
- To draw analogies between diversity in plant and human populations.

Method

Spring or early summer are the best times of year for this activity because the presence of flowers on the plants assists in identification.

Figure 17: An example worksheet for local flora studies as part of the multicultural biogeography activities.

Semi-wild habitats in the vicinity of the school are more likely to contain a good mix of both 'native' and 'introduced' plant species. If there are semi-wild areas within the school grounds, supplement studies of these with ones of nearby wasteland, scrubland, woodland, rough grassland or roadside verges. Railway embankments or derelict sidings are also excellent habitats, but usually have to be observed from a distance. Once you or the students have located suitable sites, arrange visits and give students enough copies of Figure 17 to carry out the survey at each site.

1 Spend some time exploring the patch of vegetation (preferably in the 'botanist's position' - bottom in the air, nose to the ground), and choose a plant which appeals to you.

2 Describe and draw your plant, labelling anything which makes it different from other plants.

....

....

....

3 Describe where it is growing.

....

....

4 Give your plant a name..

5 With the help of botany books and your teacher try and find out the common name (you may also discover its Latin name and that it has a number of different local names).

....

....

6 Using Richard Mabey's *Flora Britannica* and Julian Agyeman's *People, Plants and Places* try and find out where your plant came from and when and how it was introduced into Britain. These books may also tell you about whether the plant is edible, if it has any medicinal or other uses, and its importance in folklore.

....

....

....

....

7 Re-visit your plant at different times of year to record any changes you perceive, either in writing or by drawing the plant.

Visit 2 ....

....

Visit 3 ....

....

Visit 4 ....

....

	Other names	Place of origin	Approximate introduction to UK	Distinguishing characteristics
Rosebay willowherb	Bombweed Fireweed	Some native strains, some from elsewhere including Scandinavia	Not known	Each plant produces 80 000 windborne seeds – hence its phenomenal ability to spread along the rail network during the nineteenth century and to colonise city bomb sites during the Second World War
Himalayan balsam	Indian balsam Stinkypops Policeman's helmet Bee-bums	Central Asia	1839	The exploding seed pods hurl seeds up to 12m (at high velocity!). Common on canal and river banks
Sycamore	–	Central Europe	1400s	The winged wind-borne seeds make this the first tree to colonise bare ground. Aphids live on the leaves and drop sticky gunk onto cars parked underneath
Silver birch	–	Endemic – spread into Britain soon after the ice sheets retreated	About 10 000 years ago	The tiny light wind-borne seeds also enable birch to spread quickly onto bare land. Grows quickly with great potential as a biofuel. Wine can be made from the sap
Japanese knotweed	German sausage	Japan (!)	1825	Introduced as a decorative garden plant now spreading very quickly
Buddleia	–	Tibet	1890	Coming from the stony wilderness of Tibet, it thrives on waste ground. ruined buildings and stone walls. The purple flowers attract butterflies and moths in large numbers
Pineapple mayweed	Apple virgin	North America	1871	Grows on bare land, paths and even along the cracks between paving stones. The yellow flowers have no petals and smell of pineapples when crushed
Groundsel	–	Endemic	Post-glacial	One of Britain's few endemic species. Spreads easily from its abundant wind-borne seeds
Ox-eye daisy	Moon daisy Moonpenny	Mediterranean	Roman	Once common in unsprayed meadows, now making a comeback on verges and wasteland
Common ragwort	Staggerwort Stinking willie Mare's fart	Long established in the UK	Not known	Poisonous to cattle – farmers hate it and rip it up by the armful
Oxford ragwort	–	Mount Etna, Italy	1700s	Now the more common ragwort in urban areas. Introduced from Mount Etna, escaped to Oxford Railway Station in 1830 and spread along the railways to most of the UK

Figure 18: Some examples of herbs, shrubs and trees commonly occurring on urban wasteland.

Results

The following activities can be undertaken either in groups or by individual students.

- Compile a summary table of all the plants investigated by the class including an estimate of how long each has been in Britain. Figure 18 shows a summary of some commonly occurring plants found in semi-wild areas.
- On an outline map of the world show from where each student's plant originally came.
- Produce a display to show everything you have discovered about your plant.

Follow-up and interpretation

A number of discussion points could be developed concerning both ecology and multiculturalism. For example:

1 The length of time particular plants have been established in Britain may well show a gradation from long established 'native' species which spread as the ice sheets retreated, through introductions during Roman times (e.g. ground elder, ox-eye daisy, garlic mustard) to nineteenth and twentieth century arrivals such as Japanese knotweed or Himalayan balsam, thus blurring the conventional notion of 'native' and 'alien'. This observation can be seen as running parallel with the long period of successive cultural movements into Britain from elsewhere.
2 The diversity of wild plant species in cities may correlate in part with the cultural diversity.
3 Urban areas may show greater biodiversity than the surrounding countryside especially if the latter is intensively farmed.
4 Interesting and diverse plants are not confined to exotic, wild habitats.

Extension

Agyeman (1998) has devised a fun activity called a 'sticky seed walk' to demonstrate on a local scale how plants spread to new areas.

- Wearing an old pair of tights or long woollen socks over your shoes take a walk through rough grassland in summer.
- Remove tights/socks and place in a polythene bag.
- Return to the class to pick off seeds and examine under a hand lens or microscope to see how seed structure aids dispersal by humans and animals.

This can also be done by taking the dog for a walk through long grass then examining its fur.

Keep long-term records and photographs of wasteland with the help of students to enable them develop their knowledge of the main concepts of plant succession.

References and sources of information

Agyeman, J. (1995) *People, Plants and Places*. Crediton: Southgate Publishers.

Agyeman, J. (1998) 'Native good, alien bad? The city as an equal opportunity habitat', *Green Teacher*, 34, pp. 28-33.

Burn, R. (1999) 'e-geography', *Teaching Geography*, 24, 3, pp. 147-9.

Cooper, G. (1999) 'How outdoor education contributes to sustainability', *NAFSO Journal*, pp. 37-40

DfEE (1998) *Health and Safety of Pupils on Educational Visits* (ref. HSPV2). London: HMSO.

Frew, J. (1993) *Advanced Geography Fieldwork*. London: Nelson.

Harvey, P. (1991) *The Role and Value of A-level Geography Fieldwork: A Case Study*, unpublished PhD thesis, University of Durham.

Hawkins, G. (1987) 'From awareness to participation: new directions in the outdoor experience', *Geography*, 72, 3, pp. 217-22.

Job, D.A. (1996) 'Geography and environmental education: an exploration of perspectives and strategies' in Kent, A. *et al.* (eds) *Geography in Education*. Cambridge: Cambridge University Press, pp. 22-49.

Job, D.A. (1999) *New Directions in Geographical Fieldwork*. Cambridge: CUP/Queen Mary Westfield College.

Lenon, B. and Cleves, P. (1994) *Fieldwork Techniques and Projects in Geography*. London: Collins Educational.

Mabey, R. (1996) *Flora Brittanica*. London: Sinclair-Stevenson.

McNeill, C., Cory-Wright, J. and Renfrew, T. (1998) *Teaching Orienteering*. Doune: Harveys.

NAFSO (1998a) *Outdoor Education, Safety and Good Practice*. Peterborough: NAFSO.

National Association of Field Studies Officers (1998b) *Quality, Safety and Sustainability, Field Studies Centres: A Code of Practice*. Peterborough: NAFSO.

Orr, D. (1994) *Earth in Mind: On Education, Environment and the Human Prospect*. Washington DC: Island Press.

St John, P. and Richardson, D. (1996) *Methods of Statistical Analysis of Fieldwork Data* (revised edition). Sheffield: Geographical Association.

St John, P. and Richardson, D. (1997) *Methods of Presenting Fieldwork Data* (revised edition). Sheffield: Geographical Association.

Thomas, A. and May, S. (1994) *Fieldwork in Action 3: Managing Out-of-classroom Activities.* Sheffield: Geographical Association.

Van Matre, S. (1979) *Sunship Earth. An acclimatization program for outdoor learning.* Martinsville IN: American Camping Association.

Sources of information

Information on electronic links for schools can be obtained from the Virtual Teacher Centre on http://www.vtc.ngfl.gov.uk

Safe routes to schools information is available from: Sustrans (Schools), 35 King Street, Bristol BS1 4DZ. Tel: 0117 929 0888.

Young TransNet is an educational project that uses ICT and the Internet to give young people a say in transport issues. The results of local computerised surveys on how children travel to school are gathered in a national database on the project's website at http://www.yptin.org.uk

The RAC has also produced a resource entitled *Keep On Moving.* This is a self-contained classroom unit which explores the impact of travel choices on our health, safety and environment. It helps young people to review society's over-dependence on the car and to develop individual and group action plans which balance walking, cycling, using public transport and car trips. For further details call the Ignition team on 01924 298631.

Useful websites for secondary data and information:

BBC website: http://www.bbc.co.uk/weather

Department of Environment, Transport and the Regions: http://www.detr.gov.uk

Environment Agency: http://www.environment-agency.gov.uk

Meteorological Office: http://www.met-office.gov.uk

Other sources

A number of excellent geographical publications offer a range of techniques for fieldwork investigations (see, for example, Frew, 1993; Lenon and Cleves, 1994). In addition, geographical, environmental and educational journals offer a wealth of fieldwork ideas. For example, *Teaching Geography, Geography, Geography Review, Field Studies*; the occasional publications of the Field Studies Council, *Environmental Education,* past issues of *Green Teacher* and the annual *NAFSO Journal* offer case studies of practices and activities in secondary schools. Even activities aimed at more able students or devised for use at more advanced level can be adapted to meet the needs of less able or younger students working in the school locality.